RAPHAEL'S AST
Ephemeris of the
for 19

A Complete A

Mean Obliquity of the Ecliptic, 1994, 23° 26′ 24″

INTRODUCTION

Greenwich Mean Time (G.M.T.) has been used as the basis for all tabulations and times. The tabular data are for Greenwich Mean Noon (12h. G.M.T.), except for the Moon tabulations headed "MIDNIGHT". All phenomena and aspect times are now in G.M.T.

This edition follows the layout for the new form which was introduced in 1980.

BRITISH SUMMER TIME

British Summer Time begins on March 27 and ends on October 23. When *British Summer Time* (one hour in advance of G.M.T.) is used, subtract one hour from B.S.T. before entering this Ephemeris.

These dates are correct according to the acts in force at the time of printing.

Printed in Great Britain

© W. Foulsham & Co. Ltd. 1993

ISBN 0-572-01851-7

Published by
LONDON: W. FOULSHAM & CO. LTD.
YEOVIL ROAD, SLOUGH, BERKS. ENGLAND
NEW YORK   TORONTO   CAPE TOWN   SYDNEY

2					JANUARY	1994			[RAPHAEL'S	

D	D	Sidereal	☉	☉	☽	☽	☽	☽	Midnight	
M	W	Time	Long.	Dec.	Long.	Lat.	Dec.	Node	☽ Long.	☽ Dec.

		H. M. S.	° ′ ″	° ′	° ′ ″	° ′	° ′	° ′	° ′ ″	° ′
1	S	18 43 38	10♐50 50	23 S 0	25♋12 56	5 S 8	8 N17	1♐ 4	2♍11 2	5 N52
2	Su	18 47 34	11 51 58	22 55	9♍10 51	5 8	3 N22	1 1	16 12 0	0 N49
3	M	18 51 31	12 53 6	22 49	23 14 13	4 50	1 S 45	0 58	0♎17 12	4 S 18
4	T	18 55 27	13 54 15	22 43	7♎20 42	4 14	6 48	0 54	14 24 32	9 13
5	W	18 59 24	14 55 24	22 36	21 28 30	3 23	11 30	0 51	28 32 27	13 38
6	Th	19 3 21	15 56 34	22 29	5♏36 12	2 19	15 35	0 48	12♏39 36	17 17
7	F	19 7 17	16 57 43	22 22	19 42 28	1 S 7	18 45	0 45	26 44 34	19 55
8	S	19 11 14	17 58 53	22 14	3♐45 42	0 N 8	20 46	0 42	10♐45 33	21 18
9	Su	19 15 10	19 0 3	22 6	17 43 49	1 23	21 30	0 39	24 40 10	21 22
10	M	19 19 7	20 1 13	21 57	1♑34 12	2 31	20 54	0 35	8♑25 32	20 8
11	T	19 23 3	21 2 23	21 48	15 13 49	3 30	19 5	0 32	21 58 38	17 46
12	W	19 27 0	22 3 32	21 38	28 39 42	4 17	16 14	0 29	5♒16 42	14 31
13	Th	19 30 56	23 4 41	21 28	11♒49 26	4 48	12 38	0 26	18 17 46	10 37
14	F	19 34 53	24 5 49	21 17	24 41 37	5 4	8 31	0 23	1♓ 1 3	6 20
15	S	19 38 49	25 6 57	21 7	7♓16 10	5 4	4 S 8	0 20	13 27 12	1 S 54
16	Su	19 42 46	26 8 4	20 55	19 34 25	4 51	0 N20	0 16	25 38 13	2 N32
17	M	19 46 43	27 9 10	20 44	1♈39 3	4 24	4 42	0 13	7♈37 24	6 48
18	T	19 50 39	28 10 16	20 32	13 33 50	3 47	8 50	0 10	19 28 58	10 46
19	W	19 54 36	29♐11 20	20 19	25 23 27	3 0	12 36	0 7	1♉17 55	14 19
20	Th	19 58 32	0♒12 24	20 6	7♉13 3	2 5	15 53	0 4	13 9 34	17 18
21	F	20 2 29	1 13 27	19 53	19 8 7	1 N 4	18 32	0♐ 0	25 9 22	19 35
22	S	20 6 25	2 14 30	19 40	1♊ 13 58	0 0	20 24	29♏57	7♊ 22 29	21 0
23	Su	20 10 22	3 15 31	19 26	13 35 28	1 S 6	21 20	29 54	19 53 24	21 25
24	M	20 14 18	4 16 31	19 11	26 16 38	2 10	21 13	29 51	2♋45 28	20 45
25	T	20 18 15	5 17 30	18 57	9♋20 4	3 9	19 58	29 48	16 0 28	18 55
26	W	20 22 12	6 18 29	18 42	22 46 33	3 59	17 35	29 45	29 38 5	16 0
27	Th	20 26 8	7 19 26	18 26	6♌34 41	4 36	14 10	29 41	13♌35 51	12 7
28	F	20 30 5	8 20 22	18 11	20 40 57	4 58	9 53	29 38	27 49 17	7 30
29	S	20 34 1	9 21 18	17 55	5♍ 0 4	5 1	5 N 0	29 35	12♍12 31	2 N25
30	Su	20 37 58	10 22 13	17 38	19 25 50	4 46	0 S12	29 32	26 39 16	2 S 49
31	M	20 41 54	11♒23 7	17 S 22	3♎52 10	4 S 12	5 S 23	29♏29	11♎ 3 55	7 S 53

D	Mercury			Venus			Mars			Jupiter	
M	Lat.	Dec.		Lat.	Dec.		Lat.	Dec.		Lat.	Dec.

	° ′	° ′	° ′	° ′	° ′	° ′	° ′	° ′	° ′	° ′	° ′
1	1 S 40	24 S 46	24 S 42	0 S 23	23 S 38	23 S 36	0 S 50	23 S 56	23 S 53	1 N 8	13 S 41
3	1 48	24 37	24 31	0 28	23 33	23 29	0 51	23 50	23 46	1 9	13 46
5	1 54	24 23	24 13	0 32	23 25	23 20	0 51	23 42	23 38	1 9	13 52
7	1 59	24 2	23 50	0 37	23 14	23 8	0 52	23 34	23 29	1 9	13 57
9	2 3	23 36	23 20	0 41	23 1	22 53	0 53	23 25	23 19	1 9	14 2
11	2 6	23 3	22 44	0 45	22 44	22 35	0 54	23 14	23 8	1 10	14 6
13	2 7	22 24	22 2	0 49	22 25	22 14	0 55	23 3	22 56	1 10	14 11
15	2 6	21 38	21 13	0 53	22 3	21 51	0 55	22 50	22 43	1 11	14 15
17	2 3	20 47	20 19	0 57	21 38	21 25	0 56	22 36	22 29	1 11	14 19
19	1 58	19 49	19 18	1 0	21 11	20 56	0 57	22 22	22 14	1 11	14 23
21	1 50	18 46	18 12	1 3	20 41	20 25	0 57	22 6	21 58	1 11	14 27
23	1 40	17 37	17 1	1 7	20 9	19 52	0 58	21 50	21 41	1 12	14 31
25	1 28	16 24	15 45	1 10	19 34	19 16	0 59	21 32	21 23	1 12	14 34
27	1 12	15 6	14 26	1 12	18 57	18 38	0 59	21 14	21 4	1 12	14 37
29	0 53	13 46	13 S 5	1 15	18 18	17 S 58	1 0	20 54	20 S 44	1 13	14 40
31	0 S 31	12 S 24		1 S 17	17 S 37		1 S 1	20 S 34		1 N 13	14 S 43

EPHEMERIS]				JANUARY	1994									3

D	☿	♀	♂	♃	♄	♅	♆	♇	Lunar Aspects								
M	Long.	Long.	Long.	Long.	Long.	Long.	Long.	Long.	☉	☿	♀	♂	♃	♄	♅	♆	♇
1	9♐28	7♐ 7	9♐27	9♏50	27≈ 3	21♐37	20♑29	27♏ 5	⚼	⚼	⚼	⚼		☍			☐
2	11 4	8 23	10 13	9 59	27 9	21 40	20 31	27 7	△	△	△	△	⚹		⚼	⚼	
3	12 41	9 38	10 59	10 8	27 15	21 44	20 33	27 9					∠		△	△	⚹
4	14 18	10 54	11 44	10 17	27 20	21 47	20 36	27 11			☐	☐	�	⚼			∠
5	15 55	12 9	12 30	10 26	27 26	21 51	20 38	27 13	☐	☐			△		☐	☐	⎵
6	17 33	13 25	13 16	10 35	27 32	21 54	20 40	27 14					σ				
7	19 11	14 40	14 2	10 43	27 39	21 58	20 42	27 16	⚹	⚹	⚹	⚹			⚹	⚹	
8	20 49	15 56	14 48	10 52	27 45	22 1	20 45	27 18	∠	∠	∠	∠	☐		∠	∠	σ
9	22 28	17 11	15 34	11 0	27 51	22 5	20 47	27 20	⎵	⎵	⎵	⎵	⎵		⎵	⎵	
10	24 8	18 27	16 20	11 8	27 57	22 8	20 49	27 21					∠	⚹			⎵
11	25 47	19 42	17 6	11 16	28 3	22 12	20 51	27 23	σ		σ	σ	⚹	∠		σ	∠
12	27 27	20 58	17 53	11 24	28 10	22 15	20 54	27 25		σ				⎵	σ		⚹
13	29♐ 8	22 13	18 39	11 32	28 16	22 19	20 56	27 26					☐				
14	0≈49	23 29	19 25	11 39	28 23	22 23	20 58	27 28	⎵		⎵	⎵		σ	⎵	⎵	☐
15	2 30	24 44	20 11	11 47	28 29	22 26	21 1	27 29	∠	⎵	∠	∠	△		∠	∠	
16	4 11	26 0	20 58	11 54	28 36	22 30	21 3	27 31	∠			⚹			⚹	⚹	
17	5 53	27 15	21 44	12 1	28 42	22 33	21 5	27 32	⚹	⚹	⚹		⎵	⎵			△
18	7 35	28 31	22 30	12 8	28 49	22 37	21 7	27 34						∠			⎵
19	9 17	29♐46	23 17	12 15	28 55	22 40	21 10	27 35	☐		☐	☐		⚹	⚹	☐	
20	10 59	1≈ 1	24 3	12 22	29 2	22 44	21 12	27 36		☐			σ		☐		
21	12 41	2 17	24 49	12 29	29 9	22 47	21 14	27 38								△	△
22	14 22	3 32	25 36	12 35	29 15	22 51	21 16	27 39	△		△	△		☐		⎵	⎵
23	16 3	4 48	26 22	12 42	29 22	22 54	21 19	27 40	⎵	△		⎵			⎵	△	
24	17 44	6 3	27 9	12 48	29 29	22 58	21 21	27 42			⎵		⎵	△			⎵
25	19 23	7 18	27 56	12 54	29 36	23 1	21 23	27 43	⎵				△	⎵			⎵
26	21 2	8 34	28 42	13 0	29 43	23 5	21 25	27 44				σ			σ		△
27	22 38	9 49	29♐29	13 6	29 50	23 8	21 28	27 45	σ		σ		☐		σ	σ	
28	24 13	11 4	0≈15	13 11	29≈57	23 12	21 30	27 46									☐
29	25 16	12 20	1 2	13 17	0✕ 4	23 15	21 32	27 47			σ	σ			σ	⎵	⎵
30	27 16	13 35	1 49	13 22	0 11	23 19	21 34	27 49					⎵	⚹		△	△
31	28≈43	14≈50	2≈35	13♏27	0✕18	23♐22	21♐36	27♏50					⎵	△	∠		⚹

D	Saturn		Uranus		Neptune		Pluto		Mutual Aspects
M	Lat.	Dec.	Lat.	Dec.	Lat.	Dec.	Lat.	Dec.	
	°	° ′	° ′	° ′	° ′	° ′	° ′	° ′	1 ☿ σ σ´. ☿ ✱ ♃.
1	1S25	13S50	0S27	22S 9	0N37	21S16	13N46	6S 5	2 ⊙∠♄. ♀∠⚴. σ´✱♃. ♄☐♇.
3	1 25	13 46	0 27	22 8	0 37	21 16	13 47	6 5	3 ⊙ σ ♀. ♀∠♄. ☿∠♇. ♀✱♃. ♃P♄.
5	1 25	13 42	0 27	22 7	0 37	21 15	13 47	6 6	5 ♀∠♄. ♀∠♇. ☿∠♄. σ´∠♇.
7	1 25	13 37	0 27	22 6	0 37	21 14	13 48	6 6	6 ⊙ σ σ´.
9	1 25	13 33	0 27	22 5	0 37	21 14	13 48	6 6	7 ♀∠♇.
									8 ♀ σ ♆.
11	1 25	13 29	0 27	22 4	0 37	21 13	13 49	6 6	9 ☿ σ Q ♃. ☿⊥♄. ☿ σ ♅. ⊙P♅.
13	1 25	13 24	0 27	22 2	0 37	21 12	13 49	6 6	10 ☿ P σ´.
15	1 25	13 20	0 27	22 1	0 37	21 12	13 50	6 6	11 ☿ σ ♆.
17	1 25	13 15	0 27	22 0	0 37	21 11	13 51	6 6	12 ⊙⊥♄. ⊙ σ ♅. ☿✕♄. ☿✱♇. ♀ σ ♆.
19	1 25	13 11	0 27	21 59	0 37	21 11	13 51	6 6	13 ♀⊥♄. ♀ σ ♅. ♀P♀.
									14 ⊙Q ♃. ♀Q ♃. ♄⊥♅. ☿P♅.
21	1 25	13 6	0 27	21 58	0 37	21 10	13 52	6 6	15 ⊙P♅. ♀P♅.
23	1 25	13 1	0 27	21 57	0 37	21 9	13 53	6 6	16 σ´ σ ♆. ☿ P♅.
25	1 25	12 56	0 27	21 56	0 37	21 8	13 54	6 6	17 ⊙ σ ♀. ⊙✱♇. ♀✱♇. ⊙P♇.
27	1 25	12 51	0 27	21 54	0 37	21 8	13 54	6 5	18 ♀∠♄. σ´⊥♄. σ´ σ ♅.
29	1 25	12 47	0 27	21 53	0 37	21 7	13 55	6 5	19 ⊙✕♄. ♀Q♇. ♀ P♆.
31	1S25	12S42	0S28	21S52	0N37	21S 6	13N56	6S 5	20 σ´ Q ♃.
									21 ☿ ☐ ♃.
									22 σ´ P♅.
									25 σ´✱♇.
									26 ☿✕♆.
									27 ☿✕♅. ♀Q♇.
									28 σ´✕♄. ♀ P♃. σ´ P♆.
									29 ⊙Q♇.
									30 ☿⊥♃. ☿☐♇. ♀☐♃.
									31 ☿⊥♅. ☿ P♄.

4					FEBRUARY	1994			[RAPHAEL'S	
D M	D W	Sidereal Time	☉ Long.	☉ Dec.	☽ Long.	☽ Lat.	☽ Dec.	☽ Node	Midnight ☽ Long.	☽ Dec.
		H. M. S.	° ′ ″	° ′	° ′ ″	° ′	° ′	° ′	° ′ ″	° ′
1	T	20 45 51	12≈24 0	17 S 5	18≏14 3	3 S 22	10 S 16	29 ♏ 25	25≏22 10	12 S 29
2	W	20 49 47	13 24 52	16 48	2 ♏28 1	2 20	14 31	29 22	9 ♏31 25	16 20
3	Th	20 53 44	14 25 44	16 30	16 32 16	1 S 11	17 54	29 19	23 30 32	19 12
4	F	20 57 41	15 26 35	16 12	0♐26 15	0 N 3	20 12	29 16	7♐19 26	20 53
5	S	21 1 37	16 27 25	15 54	14 10 9	1 15	21 16	29 13	20 58 26	21 19
6	Su	21 5 34	17 28 14	15 36	27 44 19	2 21	21 4	29 10	4 ♑27 47	20 30
7	M	21 9 30	18 29 2	15 17	11 ♑8 49	3 20	19 39	29 6	17 47 19	18 33
8	T	21 13 27	19 29 50	14 58	24 23 13	4 6	17 12	29 3	0 ≈56 23	15 39
9	W	21 17 23	20 30 36	14 39	7≈26 40	4 39	13 55	29 0	13 53 56	12 2
10	Th	21 21 20	21 31 20	14 20	20 18 5	4 56	10 2	28 57	26 38 59	7 56
11	F	21 25 16	22 32 4	14 0	2 ♓56 34	4 59	5 46	28 54	9 ♓10 50	3 S 34
12	S	21 29 13	23 32 46	13 40	15 21 48	4 48	1 S 21	28 51	21 29 34	0 N 52
13	Su	21 33 10	24 33 26	13 20	27 34 18	4 23	3 N 3	28 47	3 ♈36 13	5 12
14	M	21 37 6	25 34 5	13 0	9 ♈35 39	3 47	7 17	28 44	15 32 57	9 16
15	T	21 41 3	26 34 42	12 39	21 28 33	3 1	11 10	28 41	27 22 57	12 57
16	W	21 44 59	27 35 18	12 19	3 ♉16 42	2 8	14 37	28 38	9 ♉10 23	16 7
17	Th	21 48 56	28 35 52	11 58	15 4 40	1 9	17 27	28 35	21 0 11	18 37
18	F	21 52 52	29≈36 24	11 37	26 57 39	0 N 7	19 35	28 31	2 ♊57 45	20 20
19	S	21 56 49	0 ♓36 54	11 15	9 ♊1 13	0 S 57	20 52	28 28	15 8 42	21 9
20	Su	22 0 45	1 37 23	10 54	21 20 55	1 59	21 10	28 25	27 38 26	20 56
21	M	22 4 42	2 37 49	10 32	4 ♋1 50	2 57	20 25	28 22	10 ♋31 33	19 38
22	T	22 8 39	3 38 14	10 10	17 7 58	3 48	18 34	28 19	23 51 17	17 14
23	W	22 12 35	4 38 37	9 48	0 ♌41 33	4 28	15 38	28 16	7 ♌38 40	13 48
24	Th	22 16 32	5 38 58	9 26	14 42 19	4 53	11 45	28 12	21 52 0	9 30
25	F	22 20 28	6 39 18	9 4	29 7 1	5 1	7 5	28 9	6 ♍26 33	4 N 33
26	S	22 24 25	7 39 35	8 42	13 ♍49 35	4 49	1 N 55	28 6	21 15 3	0 S 45
27	Su	22 28 21	8 39 51	8 19	28 41 50	4 17	3 S 25	28 3	6 ♎8 46	6 2
28	M	22 32 18	9 ♓40 5	7 S 57	13 ♎34 50	3 S 28	8 S 33	28 ♏ 0	20 ♎59 1	10 S 56

D M	Mercury Lat.	Mercury Dec.		Venus Lat.	Venus Dec.		Mars Lat.	Mars Dec.		Jupiter Lat.	Jupiter Dec.
	°	°	°	°	°	°	°	°	°	°	°
1	0 S 18	11 S 44	11 S 4	1 S 18	17 S 15	16 S 54	1 S 1	20 S 23	20 S 13	1 N 13	14 S 44
3	0 N 9	10 25	9 47	1 20	16 31	16 9	1 1	20 2	19 50	1 14	14 47
5	0 39	9 11	8 38	1 22	15 45	15 22	1 2	19 39	19 27	1 14	14 49
7	1 11	8 7	7 39	1 24	14 58	14 33	1 2	19 15	19 3	1 14	14 51
9	1 44	7 14	6 53	1 25	14 8	13 43	1 3	18 51	18 39	1 15	14 53
11	2 16	6 37	6 25	1 26	13 17	12 51	1 3	18 26	18 13	1 15	14 54
13	2 47	6 18	6 16	1 27	12 25	11 58	1 4	18 0	17 47	1 15	14 56
15	3 12	6 18	6 25	1 27	11 31	11 4	1 4	17 33	17 20	1 16	14 57
17	3 31	6 36	6 52	1 27	10 36	10 9	1 5	17 6	16 52	1 16	14 58
19	3 42	7 11	7 32	1 27	9 40	9 12	1 5	16 38	16 24	1 17	14 59
21	3 43	7 56	8 22	1 27	8 43	8 15	1 5	16 9	15 54	1 17	14 59
23	3 35	8 48	9 15	1 27	7 45	7 16	1 6	15 40	15 25	1 17	15 0
25	3 20	9 41	10 7	1 26	6 47	6 17	1 6	15 9	14 54	1 18	15 0
27	2 59	10 32	10 55	1 25	5 47	5 17	1 6	14 39	14 23	1 18	14 59
29	2 35	11 17	11 S 36	1 23	4 47	4 S 17	1 6	14 7	13 S 51	1 18	14 59
31	2 N 8	11 S 54		1 S 22	3 S 47		1 S 6	13 S 35		1 N 19	14 S 59

FULL MOON-Feb.26, 1h.15m. am. (7°♍13′)

EPHEMERIS]				FEBRUARY 1994														5
D	☿	♀	♂	♃	♄	♅	♆	♇	Lunar Aspects									
M	Long.	Long.	Long.	Long.	Long.	Long.	Long.	Long.	☉	☿	♀	♂	♃	♄	♅	♆	♇
	° ′	° ′	° ′	° ′	° ′	° ′	° ′	° ′									
1	0♓ 5	16♒ 6	3♒22	13♏32	0♓25	23♑26	21♑38	27♏51	△	⚼	△		⚺	⚼	□	□	∠
2	1 23	17 21	4 9	13 37	0 32	23 29	21 41	27 51		△		□		△			⚺
3	2 36	18 36	4 56	13 41	0 39	23 32	21 43	27 52	□		□		☌			⚹	
4	3 42	19 52	5 43	13 46	0 46	23 36	21 45	27 53		□		⚹		□	⚹	∠	☌
5	4 42	21 7	6 29	13 50	0 53	23 39	21 47	27 54	⚹				⚺		∠		
6	5 34	22 22	7 16	13 54	1 0	23 43	21 49	27 55	∠		⚹	∠	∠	⚹	⚺	⚺	⚺
7	6 17	23 37	8 3	13 58	1 7	23 46	21 51	27 56		⚹	∠	⚺	⚹	∠			∠
8	6 52	24 53	8 50	14 2	1 15	23 49	21 53	27 57	⚺	∠	⚺				☌	☌	⚹
9	7 16	26 8	9 37	14 6	1 22	23 52	21 55	27 57		⚺		☌		⚺			
10	7 31	27 23	10 24	14 9	1 29	23 56	21 57	27 58	☌				□		⚺	⚺	
11	7R 35	28 38	11 11	14 12	1 36	23 59	21 59	27 59		☌	☌			☌	∠	∠	□
12	7 28	29♒54	11 58	14 15	1 43	24 2	22 1	27 59				⚺	△				
13	7 10	1♓ 9	12 45	14 18	1 51	24 5	22 3	28 0	⚺		⚺	∠	⚼	⚺	⚹	⚹	△
14	6 42	2 24	13 32	14 21	1 58	24 9	22 5	28 0	∠	⚺		⚹					⚼
15	6 5	3 39	14 19	14 23	2 5	24 12	22 7	28 1	⚹	∠	∠			∠	□	□	
16	5 19	4 54	15 6	14 26	2 13	24 15	22 9	28 1		⚹	⚹			⚹			
17	4 26	6 9	15 53	14 28	2 20	24 18	22 11	28 2				□	☍				
18	3 26	7 24	16 40	14 30	2 27	24 21	22 13	28 2	□	□				□	△	△	☍
19	2 23	8 39	17 27	14 32	2 34	24 24	22 15	28 3			□				⚼	⚼	
20	1 16	9 54	18 15	14 33	2 42	24 27	22 17	28 3				△					
21	0♓ 9	11 9	19 2	14 35	2 49	24 30	22 19	28 3	△	△		⚼	⚼	△			
22	29♒ 3	12 24	19 49	14 36	2 56	24 33	22 21	28 4	⚼	⚼	△		△	⚼		☍	⚼
23	27 59	13 39	20 36	14 37	3 4	24 36	22 22	28 4			⚼				☍		△
24	26 59	14 54	21 23	14 38	3 11	24 39	22 24	28 4				☍	□				
25	26 3	16 9	22 10	14 38	3 18	24 42	22 26	28 4		☍				☍			□
26	25 14	17 24	22 57	14 39	3 25	24 45	22 28	28 4	☍		☍		⚹		⚼	⚼	
27	24 31	18 39	23 44	14 39	3 33	24 47	22 29	28 4					∠		△	△	⚹
28	23♒54	19♓54	24♒32	14♏39	3♓40	24♑50	22♑31	28♏ 4		⚼		⚼	⚺	⚼			∠

D	Saturn		Uranus		Neptune		Pluto	
M	Lat.	Dec.	Lat.	Dec.	Lat.	Dec.	Lat.	Dec.
	° ′	° ′	° ′	° ′	° ′	° ′	° ′	° ′
1	1S25	12S39	0S28	21S52	0N37	21S 6	13N56	6S 5
3	1 25	12 34	0 28	21 50	0 37	21 5	13 57	6 4
5	1 25	12 29	0 28	21 49	0 36	21 5	13 58	6 4
7	1 25	12 24	0 28	21 48	0 36	21 4	13 59	6 3
9	1 25	12 19	0 28	21 47	0 36	21 3	13 59	6 3
11	1 25	12 14	0 28	21 46	0 36	21 3	14 0	6 2
13	1 25	12 9	0 28	21 45	0 36	21 2	14 1	6 2
15	1 25	12 4	0 28	21 44	0 36	21 1	14 2	6 1
17	1 26	11 58	0 28	21 43	0 36	21 1	14 3	6 0
19	1 26	11 53	0 28	21 42	0 36	21 0	14 4	6 0
21	1 26	11 48	0 28	21 41	0 37	20 59	14 4	5 59
23	1 26	11 43	0 28	21 40	0 37	20 59	14 5	5 58
25	1 26	11 38	0 28	21 39	0 37	20 58	14 6	5 58
27	1 26	11 33	0 28	21 38	0 37	20 58	14 7	5 57
29	1 26	11 27	0 28	21 37	0 37	20 57	14 8	5 56
31	1S26	11S22	0S28	21S36	0N37	20S57	14N 9	5S55

1 ☿ ☌ ♄.
2 ☉ □ ♃.
3 ☉ P ♀.
6 ♀ ⚺ ♆.
7 ♀ ⚺ ♅. ♀ P ♃.
8 ☿ ∠ ♆. ☉ P ♃.
9 ♂ Q ♇.
10 ☉ ⚺ ♆. ♀ ⊥ ♆. ♀ □ ♇.
11 ☿ Stat.
12 ♀ ⊥ ♅.
13 ☉ ⚺ ♅. ☿ ∠ ♆.
14 ♀ ☌ ♄. ♀ P ♄.
15 ♂ □ ♃.
16 ☉ □ ♇. ☿ ☌ ♀.
17 ☉ ⊥ ♆. ☉ P ♄.
18 ♀ ∠ ♆.
19 ☉ ⊥ ♅. ☿ ☌ ♄.
20 ☉ ☌ ☿. ♀ ∠ ♅.
21 ☉ ☌ ♄. ☿ ⊥ ♅.
22 ☿ P ♀.
23 ☿ ⊥ ♆. ☿ □ ♇.
24 ♀ △ ♃. ☉ P ☿.
25 ♂ ⚺ ♆.
26 ☉ ∠ ♆. ♂ P ♃.
27 ☿ ⚺ ♅. ♀ P ♇.
28 ☉ ∠ ♅. ☿ ☌ ♂. ♂ ⚺ ♅. ♃ Stat.

LAST QUARTER-Feb. 3, 8h. 6m. am. (14°♏16′)

| 6 | | | | | | MARCH | | 1994 | | | | [RAPHAEL'S |

D	D	Sidereal	☉	☉	☽	☽	☽	☽		Midnight	
M	W	Time	Long.	Dec.	Long.	Lat.	Dec.	Node	☽ Long.	☽ Dec.

		H. M. S.	° ′ ″	° ′	° ′ ″	° ′	° ′	° ′	° ′ ″	° ′
1	T	22 36 14	10 ✕ 40 18	7 S 34	28 ♎ 20 29	2 S 25	13 S 9	27 ♏ 57	5 ♏ 38 34	15 S 8
2	W	22 40 11	11 40 29	7 11	12 ♏ 52 44	1 S 14	16 52	27 53	20 2 35	18 20
3	Th	22 44 8	12 40 39	6 48	27 7 55	0 N 1	19 30	27 50	4 ♐ 8 39	20 21
4	F	22 48 4	13 40 47	6 25	11 ♐ 4 48	1 15	20 52	27 47	17 56 27	21 5
5	S	22 52 1	14 40 54	6 2	24 43 46	2 22	20 58	27 44	1 ♑ 26 59	20 33
6	Su	22 55 57	15 40 59	5 39	8 ♑ 6 17	3 20	19 51	27 41	14 41 56	18 54
7	M	22 59 54	16 41 3	5 15	21 14 7	4 7	17 42	27 37	27 43 3	16 17
8	T	23 3 50	17 41 5	4 52	4 ♒ 8 54	4 40	14 41	27 34	10 ♒ 31 49	12 56
9	W	23 7 47	18 41 5	4 29	16 51 55	4 58	11 2	27 31	23 9 19	9 2
10	Th	23 11 43	19 41 3	4 5	29 24 4	5 2	6 58	27 28	5 ✕ 36 15	4 50
11	F	23 15 40	20 41 0	3 42	11 ✕ 45 55	4 51	2 S 39	27 25	17 53 9	0 S 29
12	S	23 19 37	21 40 55	3 18	23 58 2	4 27	1 N 42	27 22	0 ♈ 0 41	3 N 50
13	Su	23 23 33	22 40 47	2 54	6 ♈ 1 13	3 52	5 56	27 18	11 59 50	7 58
14	M	23 27 30	23 40 38	2 31	17 56 44	3 6	9 54	27 15	23 52 12	11 45
15	T	23 31 26	24 40 27	2 7	29 46 33	2 13	13 28	27 12	5 ♉ 40 8	15 2
16	W	23 35 23	25 40 14	1 43	11 ♉ 33 24	1 13	16 28	27 9	17 26 47	17 43
17	Th	23 39 19	26 39 58	1 20	23 20 49	0 N 11	18 47	27 6	29 16 3	19 39
18	F	23 43 16	27 39 40	0 56	5 ♊ 13 6	0 S 53	20 18	27 3	11 ♊ 12 34	20 44
19	S	23 47 12	28 39 20	0 32	17 15 8	1 55	20 55	26 59	23 21 26	20 52
20	Su	23 51 9	29 ✕ 38 58	0 S 8	29 32 8	2 53	20 33	26 56	5 ♋ 47 54	19 59
21	M	23 55 6	0 ♈ 38 34	0 N 15	12 ♋ 9 19	3 44	19 9	26 53	18 36 58	18 4
22	T	23 59 2	1 38 7	0 39	25 11 19	4 26	16 44	26 50	1 ♌ 52 45	15 19
23	W	0 2 59	2 37 38	1 3	8 ♌ 41 31	4 55	13 21	26 47	15 37 41	11 19
24	Th	0 6 55	3 37 7	1 26	22 41 11	5 7	9 7	26 43	29 51 42	6 44
25	F	0 10 52	4 36 33	1 50	7 ♍ 8 44	5 0	4 N 14	26 40	14 ♍ 31 36	1 N 38
26	S	0 14 48	5 35 57	2 13	21 59 21	4 34	1 S 1	26 37	29 30 55	3 S 41
27	Su	0 18 45	6 35 19	2 37	7 ♎ 5 7	3 48	6 18	26 34	14 ♎ 40 41	8 50
28	M	0 22 41	7 34 39	3 0	22 16 17	2 46	11 14	26 31	29 50 41	13 27
29	T	0 26 38	8 33 57	3 24	7 ♏ 22 43	1 32	15 25	26 28	14 ♏ 51 21	17 8
30	W	0 30 35	9 33 13	3 47	22 15 43	0 S 13	18 32	26 24	29 35 7	19 37
31	Th	0 34 31	10 ♈ 32 28	4 N 10	6 ♐ 49 2	1 N 6	20 S 22	26 ♏ 21	13 ♐ 57 10	20 S 46

D		Mercury			Venus			Mars			Jupiter	
M	Lat.	Dec.		Lat.	Dec.		Lat.	Dec.		Lat.	Dec.	

	° ′	° ′	° ′	° ′	° ′	° ′	° ′	° ′	° ′	° ′	° ′	
1	2 N35	11 S 17	11 S 36	1 S 23	4 S 47	4 S 17	1 S 6	14 S 7	13 S 51	1 N 18	14 S 59	
3	2 8	11 54	12 10	1 22	3 47	3 16	1 6	13 35	13 19	1 19	14 59	
5	1 40	12 24	12 35	1 20	2 46	2 15	1 7	13 3	12 47	1 19	14 58	
7	1 12	12 45	12 52	1 18	1 44	1 14	1 7	12 30	12 13	1 19	14 57	
9	0 46	12 57	13 1	1 16	0 S 43	0 S 12	1 7	11 57	11 40	1 20	14 56	
11	0 N20	13 2	13 2	1 13	0 N19	0 N50	1 7	11 23	11 6	1 20	14 54	
13	0 S 4	12 59	12 55	1 10	1 21	1 51	1 7	10 48	10 31	1 20	14 53	
15	0 26	12 49	12 41	1 7	2 22	2 53	1 7	10 14	9 56	1 21	14 51	
17	0 47	12 32	12 22	1 4	3 24	3 55	1 7	9 39	9 21	1 21	14 49	
19	1 5	12 8	11 54	1 1	4 25	4 55	1 7	9 3	8 45	1 21	14 46	
21	1 22	11 38	11 21	0 57	5 26	5 56	1 7	8 27	8 9	1 22	14 44	
23	1 37	11 2	10 42	0 53	6 26	6 56	1 7	7 51	7 33	1 22	14 41	
25	1 50	10 20	9 57	0 49	7 25	7 55	1 6	7 15	6 57	1 22	14 39	
27	2 1	9 33	9 7	0 45	8 25	8 54	1 6	6 38	6 20	1 22	14 36	
29	2 10	8 40	8 S 12	0 41	9 23	9 N52	1 6	6 2	5 S 43	1 23	14 32	
31	2 S18	7 S 42		0 S 36	10 N20		1 S 6	5 S 25		1 N 23	14 S 29	

D	☿	♀	♂	♃	♄	♅	♆	♇	Lunar Aspects								
M	Long.	Long.	Long.	Long.	Long.	Long.	Long.	Long.	☉	☿	♀	♂	♃	♄	♅	♆	♇
	° ′	° ′	° ′	° ′	° ′	° ′	° ′	° ′									
1	23♒25	21♓ 9	25♒19	14♏39	3♓47	24♑53	22♑33	28♏ 4	⚼	△		△		△	□	□	⚺
2	23R 3	22 24	26 6	14R 39	3 55	24 56	22 34	28R 4	△		⚼		☌				
3	22 48	23 39	26 53	14 39	4 2	24 58	22 36	28 4		□	△	□		□	⚹	⚹	☌
4	22 39	24 53	27 40	14 38	4 9	25 1	22 38	28 4	□				⚺		∠	∠	
5	22D 38	26 8	28 28	14 37	4 16	25 4	22 39	28 4		⚹	□	⚹	∠		⚺	⚺	⚺
6	22 43	27 23	29♒15	14 36	4 23	25 6	22 41	28 4		∠		∠	⚹	⚹			∠
7	22 53	28 38	0♓ 2	14 35	4 31	25 9	22 42	28 4	⚹	⚺				∠	☌	☌	
8	23 10	29♓52	0 49	14 33	4 38	25 11	22 44	28 3	∠		⚹	⚺		⚺			⚹
9	23 32	1♈ 7	1 36	14 32	4 45	25 14	22 45	28 3	⚺		∠		□			⚺	
10	23 59	2 22	2 24	14 30	4 52	25 16	22 47	28 3		☌	⚺	☌		☌	⚺		□
11	24 30	3 36	3 11	14 28	4 59	25 18	22 48	28 3					△		∠	∠	
12	25 6	4 51	3 58	14 26	5 6	25 21	22 50	28 2	☌	⚺			⚼		⚹	⚹	△
13	25 46	6 6	4 45	14 24	5 14	25 23	22 51	28 2		∠	☌	⚺		⚺			
14	26 30	7 20	5 32	14 21	5 21	25 25	22 52	28 1				∠		∠		□	⚼
15	27 18	8 35	6 19	14 18	5 28	25 28	22 54	28 1	⚺	⚹				⚹	□		
16	28 9	9 49	7 7	14 16	5 35	25 30	22 55	28 0	∠		⚺	⚹	☍				
17	29♒ 3	11 4	7 54	14 13	5 42	25 32	22 56	28 0	⚹		∠				△	△	☍
18	0♓ 0	12 18	8 41	14 9	5 49	25 34	22 57	27 59		□		□		□	⚼	⚼	
19	1 0	13 33	9 28	14 6	5 56	25 36	22 59	27 59			⚹						
20	2 2	14 47	10 15	14 2	6 2	25 38	23 0	27 58	□	△			⚼				
21	3 7	16 1	11 2	13 59	6 9	25 40	23 1	27 57			□	△	△	△			⚼
22	4 14	17 16	11 49	13 55	6 16	25 42	23 2	27 57		⚼		⚼		⚼	☍	☍	△
23	5 24	18 30	12 36	13 51	6 23	25 44	23 3	27 56	△				□				
24	6 35	19 44	13 24	13 46	6 30	25 46	23 4	27 55	⚼		△						□
25	7 49	20 59	14 11	13 42	6 37	25 48	23 5	27 54		☍	⚼		⚹	☍	⚼	⚼	
26	9 5	22 13	14 58	13 37	6 43	25 49	23 6	27 54				☍	∠		△	△	⚹
27	10 22	23 27	15 45	13 33	6 50	25 51	23 7	27 53	☍				⚺				∠
28	11 42	24 41	16 32	13 28	6 57	25 53	23 8	27 52		⚼	☍			⚼	□	□	⚺
29	13 3	25 55	17 19	13 23	7 3	25 54	23 9	27 51		△		⚼	☌	△			
30	14 26	27 9	18 6	13 18	7 10	25 56	23 10	27 50	⚼			△			⚹	⚹	☌
31	15♓50	28♈23	18♓53	13♏12	7♓16	25♑57	23♑11	27♏49	△				⚺	□	∠	∠	

D	Saturn		Uranus		Neptune		Pluto	
M	Lat.	Dec.	Lat.	Dec.	Lat.	Dec.	Lat.	Dec.
	° ′	° ′	° ′	° ′	° ′	° ′	° ′	° ′
1	1S26	11S27	0S28	21S37	0N37	20S57	14N 8	5S56
3	1 26	11 22	0 28	21 36	0 37	20 57	14 9	5 55
5	1 27	11 17	0 28	21 35	0 37	20 56	14 9	5 55
7	1 27	11 12	0 28	21 34	0 37	20 56	14 10	5 54
9	1 27	11 7	0 28	21 33	0 37	20 55	14 11	5 53
11	1 27	11 2	0 28	21 32	0 37	20 55	14 12	5 52
13	1 27	10 57	0 28	21 32	0 37	20 54	14 12	5 51
15	1 27	10 52	0 28	21 31	0 37	20 54	14 13	5 50
17	1 28	10 47	0 28	21 30	0 37	20 53	14 14	5 49
19	1 28	10 42	0 29	21 29	0 37	20 53	14 15	5 48
21	1 28	10 37	0 29	21 29	0 37	20 52	14 15	5 47
23	1 28	10 32	0 29	21 28	0 37	20 52	14 16	5 46
25	1 29	10 27	0 29	21 27	0 37	20 52	14 17	5 45
27	1 29	10 23	0 29	21 27	0 37	20 51	14 17	5 44
29	1 29	10 18	0 29	21 26	0 37	20 51	14 18	5 43
31	1S29	10S13	0S29	21S26	0N37	20S51	14N19	5S42

1 ☿ P ♄. ♇ Stat.
2 ☿ ⚺ ♀. ♀ ⚹ ♆.
4 ☿ ⚺ ♆. ♀ ⚹ ♅.
5 ☉ △ ♃. ♂ ⊥ ♆. ♂ □ ♇. ☉ P ♇. ☿ Stat.
6 ☿ ⚺ ♆. ☿ P ♂.
7 ☿ ⊥ ♀. ♀ △ ♇.
8 ♀ ⚼ ♃. ♂ ⊥ ♅.
10 ♀ ⚺ ♂.
12 ☿ ⚺ ♅. ♀ ⚺ ♄. ♀ Q ♆. ♂ P ♄.
13 ☉ ⚹ ♆.
14 ♀ Q ♅. ♂ ☌ ♄.
15 ♀ ± ♃. ☉ P ♀.
16 ☉ ⚹ ♅. ☿ □ ♇.
17 ☿ ⊥ ♆. ♂ ∠ ♆.
18 ☉ △ ♇. ♀ ⊥ ♄.
19 ☉ ⚼ ♃. ♀ ⚻ ♃. ♀ ⚼ ♇.
20 ☿ ⊥ ♅.
21 ♂ ∠ ♅.
22 ♀ P ♇.
23 ♀ ⊥ ♂.
24 ☿ ☌ ♄. ♂ △ ♃. ♃ Q ♅.
25 ☉ Q ♆. ☿ ∠ ♆. ☿ P ♄. ♀ P ♂.
26 ♀ ∠ ♄. ♀ ± ♇.
27 ☉ ⚺ ♄. ☿ ∠ ♅. ♀ □ ♆.
28 ☉ ± ♃. ☉ Q ♅. ☿ P ♀.
29 ☿ △ ♃. ♀ □ ♅.
30 ♂ P ♇.
31 ♀ ⚻ ♇. ♀ P ♄.

| 8 | | | | | APRIL | | 1994 | | | [RAPHAEL'S |

D	D	Sidereal	☉	☉	☽	☽	☽	☽		Midnight	
M	W	Time	Long.	Dec.	Long.	Lat.	Dec.	Node		☽ Long.	☽ Dec.

		H. M. S.	° ′ ″	° ′	° ′ ″	° ′	° ′	° ′		° ′ ″	° ′
1	F	0 38 28	11 ♈ 31 41	4 N34	20 ✗ 59 18	2 N18	20 S 50	26 ♏ 18		27 ✗ 55 27	20 S 35
2	S	0 42 24	12 30 52	4 57	4 ♑ 45 42	3 20	20 1	26 15		11 ♑ 30 14	19 10
3	Su	0 46 21	13 30 1	5 20	18 9 19	4 10	18 5	26 12		24 43 16	16 46
4	M	0 50 17	14 29 9	5 43	1 ♒ 12 24	4 45	15 15	26 9		7 ♒ 37 7	13 34
5	T	0 54 14	15 28 14	6 5	13 57 45	5 5	11 46	26 5		20 14 40	9 50
6	W	0 58 10	16 27 18	6 28	26 28 12	5 10	7 49	26 2		2 ♓ 38 41	5 45
7	Th	1 2 7	17 26 20	6 51	8 ♓ 46 25	5 1	3 S 38	25 59		14 51 41	1 S 29
8	F	1 6 4	18 25 20	7 13	20 54 44	4 38	0 N40	25 56		26 55 49	2 N47
9	S	1 10 0	19 24 19	7 36	2 ♈ 55 9	4 3	4 53	25 53		8 ♈ 52 59	6 55
10	Su	1 13 57	20 23 15	7 58	14 49 31	3 18	8 53	25 49		20 44 58	10 45
11	M	1 17 53	21 22 9	8 20	26 39 35	2 24	12 31	25 46		2 ♉ 33 35	14 9
12	T	1 21 50	22 21 2	8 42	8 ♉ 27 15	1 24	15 39	25 43		14 20 52	16 59
13	W	1 25 46	23 19 52	9 4	20 14 45	0 N20	18 8	25 40		26 9 15	19 6
14	Th	1 29 43	24 18 40	9 25	2 ♊ 4 44	0 S 45	19 51	25 37		8 ♊ 1 37	20 23
15	F	1 33 39	25 17 26	9 47	14 0 21	1 48	20 42	25 34		20 1 25	20 46
16	S	1 37 36	26 16 10	10 8	26 5 18	2 48	20 35	25 30		2 ♋ 12 32	20 10
17	Su	1 41 33	27 14 52	10 30	8 ♋ 23 39	3 41	19 30	25 27		14 39 12	18 35
18	M	1 45 29	28 13 32	10 51	20 59 42	4 24	17 27	25 24		27 25 41	16 4
19	T	1 49 26	29 ♈ 12 9	11 11	3 ♌ 57 37	4 56	14 28	25 21		10 ♌ 35 53	12 39
20	W	1 53 22	0 ♉ 10 44	11 32	17 20 50	5 13	10 39	25 18		24 12 40	8 29
21	Th	1 57 19	1 9 17	11 53	1 ♍ 11 29	5 13	6 10	25 14		8 ♍ 17 11	3 N44
22	F	2 1 15	2 7 48	12 13	15 29 33	4 53	1 N12	25 11		22 48 8	1 S 22
23	S	2 5 12	3 6 16	12 33	0 ♎ 12 19	4 14	3 S 58	25 8		7 ♎ 41 18	6 32
24	Su	2 9 8	4 4 43	12 53	15 14 6	3 17	9 2	25 5		22 49 36	11 24
25	M	2 13 5	5 3 7	13 12	0 ♏ 26 37	2 6	13 35	25 2		8 ♏ 3 53	15 33
26	T	2 17 2	6 1 30	13 32	15 40 7	0 S 45	17 15	24 59		23 14 9	18 38
27	W	2 20 58	6 59 51	13 51	0 ✗ 44 51	0 N38	19 41	24 55		8 ✗ 11 14	20 22
28	Th	2 24 55	7 58 10	14 10	15 32 30	1 58	20 42	24 52		22 47 58	20 41
29	F	2 28 51	8 56 28	14 29	29 57 13	3 7	20 19	24 49		6 ♑ 59 54	19 38
30	S	2 32 48	9 ♉ 54 44	14 N47	13 ♑ 55 56	4 N 3	18 S 40	24 ♏ 46		20 ♑ 45 18	17 S 27

D		Mercury		Venus		Mars		Jupiter	
M	Lat.	Dec.		Lat.	Dec.		Lat.	Dec.		Lat.	Dec.

M	Lat.		Dec.		Lat.		Dec.		Lat.		Dec.		Lat.	Dec.
	° ′	° ′	° ′		° ′	° ′	° ′		° ′	° ′	° ′		° ′	° ′
1	2 S 20	7 S 11		0 S 34	10 N49		1 S 6	5 S 6		1 N 23	14 S 27
3	2 25	6 6	6 S 39	0 29	11 45	11 N17	1 5	4 29	4 S 48	1 23	14 24
5	2 27	4 56	5 31	0 24	12 40	12 12	1 5	3 52	4 10	1 23	14 20
7	2 28	3 41	4 19	0 19	13 33	13 7	1 5	3 14	3 33	1 24	14 16
9	2 26	2 22	3 2	0 14	14 26	14 0	1 4	2 37	2 55	1 24	14 12
			1 41			14 51			2 18		
11	2 23	0 S 59		0 9	15 16		1 4	1 59		1 24	14 8
13	2 18	0 N29	0 S 15	0 S 4	16 6	15 41	1 4	1 22	1 40	1 24	14 4
15	2 0	2 0	1 N 14	0 N 0	16 54	16 30	1 3	0 44	1 3	1 24	13 59
17	2 1	3 34	2 47	0 7	17 40	17 17	1 3	0 S 7	0 S 25	1 24	13 55
19	1 49	5 12	4 23	0 12	18 24	18 2	1 2	0 N31	0 N 12	1 24	13 51
			6 1			18 45			0 50		
21	1 36	6 52		0 18	19 6		1 2	1 8		1 24	13 46
23	1 20	8 34	7 43	0 23	19 47	19 27	1 1	1 45	1 27	1 24	13 41
25	1 3	10 18	9 26	0 29	20 25	20 6	1 0	2 23	2 4	1 24	13 37
27	0 44	12 1	11 10	0 34	21 1	20 43	1 0	3 0	2 41	1 24	13 32
29	0 24	13 44	12 53	0 39	21 35	21 18	0 59	3 36	3 18	1 24	13 27
31	0 S 4	15 N25	14 N 35	0 N 45	22 N 6	21 N51	0 S 58	4 N13	3 N 55	1 N 24	13 S 23

FULL MOON-Apr.25, 7h.45m. pm. (5°♏22′)

D M	☿ Long. ° ′	♀ Long. ° ′	♂ Long. ° ′	♃ Long. ° ′	♄ Long. ° ′	♅ Long. ° ′	♆ Long. ° ′	♇ Long. ° ′
1	17♓16	29♈37	19♓40	13♏ 7	7♓23	25♑59	23♑12	27♏48
2	18 44	0♉51	20 27	13R 1	7 29	26 0	23 12	27R 47
3	20 13	2 5	21 14	12 56	7 36	26 2	23 13	27 46
4	21 44	3 19	22 0	12 50	7 42	26 3	23 14	27 45
5	23 16	4 33	22 47	12 44	7 48	26 4	23 14	27 44
6	24 50	5 47	23 34	12 38	7 55	26 6	23 15	27 43
7	26 26	7 1	24 21	12 32	8 1	26 7	23 16	27 42
8	28 3	8 15	25 8	12 25	8 7	26 8	23 16	27 41
9	29♓41	9 28	25 55	12 19	8 13	26 9	23 17	27 39
10	1♈21	10 42	26 41	12 12	8 19	26 10	23 17	27 38
11	3 3	11 56	27 28	12 6	8 25	26 11	23 18	27 37
12	4 46	13 10	28 15	11 59	8 31	26 12	23 18	27 36
13	6 31	14 23	29 2	11 52	8 37	26 13	23 19	27 34
14	8 17	15 37	29♓48	11 45	8 43	26 14	23 19	27 33
15	10 4	16 50	0♈35	11 38	8 49	26 15	23 19	27 32
16	11 54	18 4	1 22	11 31	8 54	26 15	23 20	27 30
17	13 44	19 17	2 8	11 24	9 0	26 16	23 20	27 29
18	15 37	20 31	2 55	11 17	9 6	26 17	23 20	27 28
19	17 31	21 44	3 41	11 9	9 11	26 17	23 20	27 26
20	19 26	22 58	4 28	11 2	9 17	26 18	23 21	27 25
21	21 23	24 11	5 14	10 54	9 22	26 18	23 21	27 23
22	23 22	25 24	6 1	10 47	9 28	26 19	23 21	27 22
23	25 22	26 38	6 47	10 40	9 33	26 19	23 21	27 21
24	27 24	27 51	7 33	10 32	9 38	26 20	23 21	27 19
25	29♈27	29♉ 4	8 20	10 24	9 43	26 20	23R 21	27 18
26	1♉31	0♊17	9 6	10 17	9 48	26 20	23 21	27 16
27	3 37	1 30	9 52	10 9	9 53	26 20	23 21	27 15
28	5 43	2 43	10 38	10 2	9 58	26 20	23 21	27 13
29	7 51	3 56	11 24	9 54	10 3	26 21	23 21	27 11
30	10♉ 0	5♊ 9	12♈11	9♏46	10♓ 8	26♑21	23♑21	27♏10

D	Lunar Aspects ☉	☿	♀	♂	♃	♄	♅	♆	♇
1		□	⚼	□			⚺	⚺	⚺
2			△		∠	⚹			
3	□	⚹		⚹	⚹	∠		☌	∠
4		∠	□	∠			☌		⚹
5	⚹				□	⚺			
6	∠	⚺		⚺			⚺	⚺	□
7			⚹		△	☌	∠	∠	
8	⚺		∠	☌			⚹	⚹	
9		☌			⚼	⚺			△
10			⚺						⚼
11	☌			⚺		∠	□	□	
12		⚺	●	∠	☍	⚹			
13	⚺	∠						△	
14				⚹			△		☍
15	∠	⚹	⚺			□	⚼	⚼	
16	⚹			□	⚼				
17			∠		△	△			⚼
18		□	⚹			⚼	☍	☍	
19	□			△					△
20		△	□	⚼	□				
21	△	⚼							□
22	⚼				⚹	☍	⚼	⚼	
23			△	☍	∠		△	△	⚹
24			⚼		⚺				∠
25	☍	☍				⚼	□	□	⚺
26					☌	△			
27			☍	⚼			⚹	⚹	☌
28		⚼		△	⚺	□	∠	∠	
29	⚼				∠		⚺	⚺	⚺
30	△	△		□	⚹	⚹			∠

D M	Saturn Lat. ° ′	Saturn Dec. ° ′	Uranus Lat. ° ′	Uranus Dec. ° ′	Neptune Lat. ° ′	Neptune Dec. ° ′	Pluto Lat. ° ′	Pluto Dec. ° ′
1	1S29	10S11	0S29	21S25	0N37	20S51	14N19	5S42
3	1 30	10 7	0 29	21 25	0 37	20 50	14 20	5 41
5	1 30	10 2	0 29	21 25	0 37	20 50	14 20	5 40
7	1 30	9 58	0 29	21 24	0 37	20 50	14 21	5 39
9	1 31	9 53	0 29	21 24	0 37	20 50	14 21	5 38
11	1 31	9 49	0 29	21 23	0 37	20 49	14 22	5 37
13	1 31	9 45	0 29	21 23	0 37	20 49	14 22	5 36
15	1 32	9 41	0 29	21 23	0 37	20 49	14 23	5 35
17	1 32	9 37	0 29	21 23	0 37	20 49	14 23	5 34
19	1 32	9 33	0 30	21 23	0 37	20 49	14 23	5 33
21	1 33	9 29	0 30	21 22	0 37	20 49	14 24	5 32
23	1 33	9 25	0 30	21 22	0 37	20 49	14 24	5 31
25	1 33	9 22	0 30	21 22	0 37	20 49	14 24	5 30
27	1 34	9 18	0 30	21 22	0 37	20 49	14 24	5 30
29	1 34	9 15	0 30	21 22	0 37	20 49	14 25	5 29
31	1S34	9S12	0S30	21S22	0N37	20S49	14N25	5S28

2 ☉▽♃. ☉⚼♇. ☉P♂.
3 ☉⊥♄.
4 ☿☌♂. ☉P☿. ☉P♇. ☿P♇.
5 ☿⚹♆.
6 ♂⚹♆.
7 ☿⚹♅.
8 ☿⚼♃. ☿△♇. ♀⚹♄. ☿P♂.
9 ♂⚹♅. ♀P♃.
10 ♄∠♆.
11 ☉±♇. ♀☍♃. ♂⚼♃. ♂△♇.
12 ☿Q♆. ♀∠♂.
13 ☉∠♄. ☉□♆. ☿±♃.
14 ☿⚺♄. ☿Q♅. ☿P♂.
15 ☉P♄.
16 ☉□♅. ☿⊥♀. ☿▽♃. ☿⚼♇.
17 ☉▽♇.
18 ☿⊥♄. ♃Q♆.
19 ♀Q♄. ☿P♇.
20 ♀△♆.
21 ☿±♇. ♂±♃. ♂Q♆.
22 ☿□♆.
23 ☿∠♄. ☿□♅. ♀△♅.
24 ☿▽♇. ♀☍♇. ☿P♄.
25 ☿⚺♀. ♂Q♅. ♆Stat.
26 ☉P♃. ♀P♆.
27 ♂▽♃. ♂⚺♄.
28 ♃△♄. ♀P♅.
29 ☿P♃.
30 ☉☌☿. ☉☍♃. ☉⚹♄. ☿☍♃. ☿⚹♄.
♂⚼♇. ☉P☿. ♅Stat.

LAST QUARTER-Apr. 3, 2h.55m. am. (13°♑ 8′)

| 10 | | | | | | MAY | 1994 | | | | [RAPHAEL'S |

D	D	Sidereal	☉		☉	☽	☽	☽	☽	Midnight	
M	W	Time	Long.		Dec.	Long.	Lat.	Dec.	Node	☽ Long.	☽ Dec.

		H. M. S.	° ′ ″		° ′	° ′ ″	° ′	° ′	° ′	° ′	° ′
1	Su	2 36 44	10 ♉ 52 59	15 N 5	27 ⯞ 28 9	4 N44	16 S 1	24 ♏ 43	4 ≈ 4 45	14 S 24
2	M	2 40 41	11 51 12	15 23	10 ≈ 35 23	5 9	12 37	24 40	17 0 28	10 44
3	T	2 44 37	12 49 23	15 41	23 20 27	5 17	8 44	24 36	29 35 47	6 41
4	W	2 48 34	13 47 34	15 59	5 ⋎ 46 56	5 10	4 35	24 33	11 ⋎ 54 24	2 S 27
5	Th	2 52 31	14 45 42	16 16	17 58 40	4 50	0 S 18	24 30	24 0 11	1 N 49
6	F	2 56 27	15 43 50	16 33	29 59 25	4 16	3 N 55	24 27	5 ⋎ 56 47	5 58
7	S	3 0 24	16 41 55	16 50	11 ⋎ 52 42	3 32	7 57	24 24	17 47 32	9 52
8	Su	3 4 20	17 40 0	17 6	23 41 38	2 40	11 40	24 20	29 35 21	13 22
9	M	3 8 17	18 38 2	17 22	5 ♉ 29 0	1 40	14 55	24 17	11 ♉ 22 53	16 20
10	T	3 12 13	19 36 4	17 38	17 17 17	0 N 36	17 34	24 14	23 12 28	18 38
11	W	3 16 10	20 34 3	17 54	29 8 43	0 S 30	19 29	24 11	5 ♊ 6 19	20 7
12	Th	3 20 6	21 32 1	18 9	11 ♊ 5 31	1 35	20 32	24 8	17 6 36	20 43
13	F	3 24 3	22 29 58	18 24	23 9 53	2 36	20 40	24 5	29 15 38	20 21
14	S	3 28 0	23 27 53	18 38	5 ♋ 24 12	3 31	19 48	24 1	11 ♋ 35 52	19 1
15	Su	3 31 56	24 25 46	18 53	17 51 0	4 18	17 59	23 58	24 9 55	16 44
16	M	3 35 53	25 23 38	19 7	0 ♌ 32 59	4 52	15 16	23 55	7 ♌ 0 32	13 36
17	T	3 39 49	26 21 27	19 20	13 32 53	5 13	11 45	23 52	20 10 20	9 44
18	W	3 43 46	27 19 15	19 34	26 53 8	5 17	7 34	23 49	3 ♍ 41 29	5 17
19	Th	3 47 42	28 17 1	19 47	10 ♍ 35 31	5 4	2 N 54	23 46	17 35 16	0 N 26
20	F	3 51 39	29 ♉ 14 46	19 59	24 40 40	4 33	2 S 4	23 42	1 ♎ 51 31	4 S 34
21	S	3 55 35	0 ♊ 12 29	20 12	9 ♎ 7 29	3 44	7 3	23 39	16 28 5	9 27
22	Su	3 59 32	1 10 10	20 24	23 52 44	2 39	11 44	23 36	1 ♏ 20 38	13 51
23	M	4 3 29	2 7 50	20 35	8 ♏ 50 55	1 S 22	15 45	23 33	16 22 36	17 24
24	T	4 7 25	3 5 29	20 46	23 54 37	0 N 1	18 45	23 30	1 ✗ 25 53	19 46
25	W	4 11 22	4 3 6	20 57	8 ✗ 55 19	1 23	20 25	23 26	16 21 51	20 43
26	Th	4 15 18	5 0 42	21 8	23 44 31	2 39	20 39	23 23	1 ⯞ 2 28	20 14
27	F	4 19 15	5 58 17	21 18	8 ⯞ 14 59	3 42	19 29	23 20	15 21 31	18 26
28	S	4 23 11	6 55 51	21 28	22 21 38	4 31	17 8	23 17	29 15 8	15 36
29	Su	4 27 8	7 53 24	21 37	6 ≈ 1 54	5 2	13 53	23 14	12 ≈ 42 2	12 1
30	M	4 31 4	8 50 56	21 47	19 15 41	5 16	10 2	23 11	25 43 10	7 58
31	T	4 35 1	9 ♊ 48 28	21 N55	2 ✗ 4 53	5 N13	5 S 51	23 ♏ 7	8 ✗ 21 16	3 S 42

D	Mercury			Venus			Mars			Jupiter	
M	Lat.	Dec.		Lat.	Dec.		Lat.	Dec.		Lat.	Dec.

	° ′	° ′	° ′	° ′	° ′	° ′	° ′	° ′	° ′	° ′	° ′
1	0 S 4	15 N25	16 N 14	0 N 45	22 N 6	22 N21	0 S 58	4 N13	4 N 31	1 N 24	13 S 23
3	0 N18	17 2	17 49	0 50	22 35	22 49	0 58	4 49	5 7	1 24	13 18
5	0 39	18 34	19 17	0 55	23 2	23 14	0 57	5 25	5 43	1 23	13 13
7	0 59	19 59	20 38	1 0	23 26	23 37	0 56	6 1	6 19	1 23	13 9
9	1 18	21 15	21 50	1 5	23 47	23 57	0 55	6 37	6 54	1 23	13 4
11	1 35	22 22	22 52	1 10	24 6	24 14	0 55	7 12	7 29	1 23	13 0
13	1 50	23 19	23 43	1 14	24 22	24 29	0 54	7 47	8 4	1 23	12 55
15	2 2	24 7	24 25	1 19	24 35	24 41	0 53	8 21	8 38	1 22	12 51
17	2 11	24 42	24 56	1 23	24 45	24 49	0 52	8 55	9 12	1 22	12 47
19	2 17	25 9	25 18	1 27	24 53	24 56	0 51	9 29	9 46	1 22	12 42
21	2 19	25 26	25 32	1 31	24 58	24 59	0 50	10 2	10 19	1 21	12 38
23	2 18	25 35	25 37	1 35	24 59	24 59	0 49	10 35	10 52	1 21	12 35
25	2 14	25 37	25 35	1 39	24 58	24 57	0 48	11 8	11 24	1 21	12 31
27	2 6	25 32	25 27	1 42	24 54	24 51	0 47	11 40	11 55	1 20	12 27
29	1 55	25 21	25 N13	1 45	24 48	24 43	0 46	12 11	12 N 27	1 20	12 24
31	1 N40	25 N 5		1 N 48	24 N38		0 S 45	12 N42		1 N 19	12 S 21

FULL MOON-May 25, 3h.39m. am. (3°♐43′)

D M	☿ Long.	♀ Long.	♂ Long.	♃ Long.	♄ Long.	♅ Long.	♆ Long.	♇ Long.	☉	☿	♀	♂	♃	♄	♅	♆	♇
	° ′	° ′	° ′	° ′	° ′	° ′	° ′	° ′									
1	12♉ 9	6♊22	12♈57	9♏39	10♓13	26♑21	23♑20	27♏ 8			⚼			∠	☌	☌	✱
2	14 18	7 35	13 43	9R 31	10 18	26R 21	23R 20	27R 7	□	□	△	✱	□	⊻			
3	16 28	8 48	14 29	9 23	10 22	26 20	23 20	27 5							⊻	⊻	□
4	18 37	10 1	15 15	9 16	10 27	26 20	23 20	27 4			□	∠	△	☌	∠	∠	
5	20 47	11 13	16 1	9 8	10 31	26 20	23 19	27 2	✱	✱		⊻				✱	
6	22 55	12 26	16 47	9 0	10 36	26 20	23 19	27 0	∠				⚼		✱		△
7	25 2	13 39	17 32	8 53	10 40	26 20	23 19	26 59	⊻	∠	✱			⊻			⚼
8	27 9	14 51	18 18	8 45	10 44	26 19	23 18	26 57		⊻		☌		∠	□	□	
9	29♉13	16 4	19 4	8 38	10 48	26 19	23 18	26 55			∠		☍	✱			
10	1♊16	17 17	19 50	8 30	10 53	26 18	23 17	26 54	●		⊻	⊻					
11	3 16	18 29	20 36	8 23	10 57	26 18	23 17	26 52		☌					△	△	☍
12	5 15	19 42	21 21	8 16	11 1	26 17	23 16	26 50				∠		□	⚼	⚼	
13	7 10	20 54	22 7	8 9	11 4	26 17	23 16	26 49	⊻		☌	✱	⚼				
14	9 4	22 6	22 52	8 1	11 8	26 16	23 15	26 47	∠	⊻			△	△			
15	10 54	23 19	23 38	7 54	11 12	26 15	23 15	26 45			⊻	□				☍	⚼
16	12 41	24 31	24 23	7 47	11 15	26 15	23 14	26 44	✱	∠				⚼	☍		△
17	14 25	25 43	25 9	7 40	11 19	26 14	23 13	26 42		✱	∠		□				
18	16 7	26 55	25 54	7 33	11 22	26 13	23 13	26 40	□		✱	△					□
19	17 44	28 8	26 39	7 27	11 26	26 12	23 12	26 39				⚼	✱	☍	⚼	⚼	
20	19 19	29♊20	27 25	7 20	11 29	26 11	23 11	26 37	△	□	□		∠		△	△	✱
21	20 50	0♋32	28 10	7 13	11 32	26 10	23 10	26 35	⚼				⊻				∠
22	22 18	1 44	28 55	7 7	11 35	26 9	23 9	26 34		△		☍		⚼	□	□	⊻
23	23 43	2 56	29♈40	7 0	11 38	26 8	23 9	26 32		⚼	△		☌	△			
24	25 4	4 7	0♉25	6 54	11 41	26 7	23 8	26 31			⚼				✱	✱	☌
25	26 21	5 19	1 10	6 48	11 44	26 6	23 7	26 29	●–●				⊻	□	∠	∠	
26	27 35	6 31	1 55	6 42	11 47	26 5	23 6	26 27		☍		⚼	∠		⊻	⊻	⊻
27	28 46	7 43	2 40	6 36	11 49	26 4	23 5	26 26			☍	△	✱	✱			∠
28	29♊52	8 54	3 25	6 30	11 52	26 2	23 4	26 24	⚼					∠	☌	☌	✱
29	0♋55	10 6	4 10	6 25	11 54	26 1	23 3	26 22	△			□	□	⊻			
30	1 54	11 17	4 54	6 19	11 57	26 0	23 2	26 21		⚼						⊻	
31	2♋50	12♋29	5♉39	6♏14	11♓59	25♑58	23♑ 1	26♏19		△	⚼	✱	△		⊻	∠	□

D M	Saturn Lat.	Saturn Dec.	Uranus Lat.	Uranus Dec.	Neptune Lat.	Neptune Dec.	Pluto Lat.	Pluto Dec.
	° ′	° ′	° ′	° ′	° ′	° ′	° ′	° ′
1	1S34	9S12	0S30	21S22	0N37	20S49	14N25	5S28
3	1 35	9 8	0 30	21 22	0 37	20 49	14 25	5 27
5	1 35	9 5	0 30	21 23	0 37	20 49	14 25	5 26
7	1 36	9 2	0 30	21 23	0 37	20 49	14 25	5 26
9	1 36	9 0	0 30	21 23	0 37	20 49	14 25	5 25
11	1 36	8 57	0 30	21 23	0 37	20 49	14 25	5 24
13	1 37	8 54	0 30	21 23	0 37	20 49	14 25	5 23
15	1 37	8 52	0 30	21 24	0 37	20 50	14 25	5 23
17	1 38	8 50	0 30	21 24	0 37	20 50	14 25	5 22
19	1 38	8 47	0 30	21 24	0 37	20 50	14 25	5 22
21	1 39	8 45	0 31	21 25	0 37	20 50	14 25	5 21
23	1 39	8 43	0 31	21 25	0 37	20 50	14 24	5 21
25	1 39	8 42	0 31	21 26	0 37	20 51	14 24	5 20
27	1 40	8 40	0 31	21 26	0 37	20 51	14 24	5 20
29	1 40	8 39	0 31	21 27	0 37	20 51	14 23	5 19
31	1S41	8S37	0S31	21S27	0N37	20S52	14N23	5S19

2 ☿⊻♂.
3 ♀▽♃. ♀⚼♆.
4 ♀□♄.
5 ♀⚼♅. ♂P♇.
6 ☿⊥♂. ☿Q♄. ☿△♆. ♂⊥♄.
8 ☿△♅. ☿☍♇. ♀±♃. ☿P♆.
9 ☿P♅.
10 ♀±♆.
11 ☉⊻♂. ♂±♇.
12 ♀±♅.
13 ☿∠♂. ☿▽♃.
14 ☉Q♄. ☉△♆. ☿⚼♆. ♂□♆.
15 ☿□♄. ☿⚼♅. ♀⚼♃. ♀▽♆.
16 ♀✱♂. ♄∠♅.
17 ☉△♅. ☉☍♇. ☿±♃. ♀▽♅. ☿P♀.
♂P♄.
18 ♀▽♇. ♂□♅.
19 ☿±♆. ♂∠♄. ♂▽♇.
20 ☉⊻♀.
21 ☿±♅.
22 ☿⚼♃.
23 ☿▽♆. ♀±♇.
24 ☉P♆.
25 ☿▽♅. ☿▽♇.
26 ♀△♃.
28 ☉▽♃. ☉P♅.
29 ☉⚼♆.
30 ☿±♇. ♀⚼♇. ♂P♃.
31 ♀△♄.

LAST QUARTER-May 2, 2h.32m. pm. (11°♒57′)

12					JUNE	1994				[RAPHAEL'S	
D	D	Sidereal	⊙	⊙	☽	☽	☽	☽		Midnight	
M	W	Time	Long.	Dec.	Long.	Lat.	Dec.	Node		☽ Long.	☽ Dec.

D M	D W	H. M. S.	⊙ Long. ° ′ ″	⊙ Dec. ° ′	☽ Long. ° ′ ″	☽ Lat. ° ′	☽ Dec. ° ′	☽ Node ° ′	☽ Long. ° ′ ″	☽ Dec. ° ′
1	W	4 38 58	10 Ⅱ 45 58	22 N 4	14 ♓ 32 51	4 N56	1 S 32	23 ♏ 4	20 ♓ 40 11	0 N38
2	Th	4 42 54	11 43 28	22 11	26 43 49	4 26	2 N46	23 1	2 ♈ 44 21	4 51
3	F	4 46 51	12 40 56	22 19	8 ♈ 42 22	3 44	6 53	22 58	14 38 26	8 50
4	S	4 50 47	13 38 25	22 26	20 33 7	2 54	10 42	22 55	26 26 56	12 28
5	Su	4 54 44	14 35 52	22 33	2 ♉ 20 25	1 56	14 6	22 52	8 ♉ 14 1	15 35
6	M	4 58 40	15 33 19	22 39	14 8 11	0 N53	16 56	22 48	20 3 21	18 5
7	T	5 2 37	16 30 45	22 45	25 59 52	0 S 12	19 22	22 45	1 Ⅱ 58 3	19 49
8	W	5 6 33	17 28 10	22 51	7 Ⅱ 58 14	1 17	20 22	22 42	14 0 39	20 40
9	Th	5 10 30	18 25 34	22 56	20 5 33	2 20	20 45	22 39	26 13 7	20 34
10	F	5 14 27	19 22 58	23 1	2 ♋ 23 31	3 17	20 8	22 36	8 ♋ 36 54	19 28
11	S	5 18 23	20 20 21	23 5	14 53 25	4 5	18 33	22 32	21 13 9	17 24
12	Su	5 22 20	21 17 43	23 9	27 36 13	4 42	16 2	29	4 ♌ 2 42	14 27
13	M	5 26 16	22 15 4	23 13	10 ♌ 32 41	5 5	12 41	22 26	17 6 16	10 45
14	T	5 30 13	23 12 24	23 16	23 43 32	5 13	8 41	22 23	0 ♍ 24 33	6 28
15	W	5 34 9	24 9 43	23 19	7 ♍ 9 23	5 4	4 N10	22 20	13 58 6	1 N47
16	Th	5 38 6	25 7 2	23 21	20 50 44	4 38	0 S 38	22 17	27 47 17	3 S 5
17	F	5 42 2	26 4 19	23 23	4 ♎ 47 44	3 55	5 30	22 13	11 ♎ 51 59	7 53
18	S	5 45 59	27 1 35	23 24	18 59 52	2 57	10 22	22 10	26 11 11	12 20
19	Su	5 49 56	27 58 51	23 25	3 ♏ 25 36	1 47	14 20	22 7	10 ♏ 42 42	16 8
20	M	5 53 52	28 56 6	23 26	18 1 57	0 S 29	17 40	22 4	25 22 45	18 56
21	T	5 57 49	29 Ⅱ 53 20	23 26	2 ♐ 44 23	0 N51	19 53	22 1	10 ♐ 6 5	20 29
22	W	6 1 45	0 ♋ 50 34	23 26	17 27 0	2 7	20 44	21 58	24 46 15	20 38
23	Th	6 5 42	1 47 48	23 26	2 ♑ 2 59	3 15	20 11	21 54	9 ♑ 16 22	19 42
24	F	6 9 38	2 45 1	23 25	16 25 38	4 9	18 19	21 51	23 30 5	16 58
25	S	6 13 35	3 42 13	23 23	0 ♒ 29 12	4 46	15 23	21 48	7 ♒ 22 32	13 37
26	Su	6 17 31	4 39 26	23 21	14 9 48	5 6	11 41	21 45	20 50 52	9 39
27	M	6 21 28	5 36 38	23 19	27 25 45	5 9	7 31	21 42	3 ♓ 54 34	5 21
28	T	6 25 25	6 33 50	23 17	10 ♓ 17 35	4 56	3 S 8	21 38	16 35 8	0 S56
29	W	6 29 21	7 31 2	23 14	22 47 41	4 29	1 N15	21 35	28 55 45	3 N25
30	Th	6 33 18	8 ♋ 28 15	23 N10	4 ♈ 59 53	3 N50	5 N30	21 ♏ 32	11 ♈ 0 42	7 N32

D M	Mercury			Venus			Mars			Jupiter	
	Lat.	Dec.		Lat.	Dec.		Lat.	Dec.		Lat.	Dec.
	° ′	° ′	° ′	° ′	° ′	° ′	° ′	° ′	° ′	° ′	° ′
1	1 N32	24 N55	24 N 44	1 N 49	24 N32	24 N26	0 S 44	12 N57	13 N 12	1 N 19	12 S 19
3	1 12	24 32	24 19	1 51	24 19	24 11	0 43	13 27	13 42	1 19	12 16
5	0 49	24 6	23 52	1 53	24 2	23 53	0 42	13 57	14 11	1 18	12 14
7	0 N23	23 37	23 22	1 55	23 43	23 33	0 41	14 26	14 40	1 18	12 11
9	0 S 5	23 6	22 51	1 56	23 22	23 10	0 40	14 54	15 8	1 17	12 9
11	0 36	22 34	22 18	1 57	22 57	22 44	0 39	15 22	15 35	1 17	12 7
13	1 9	22 2	21 45	1 58	22 31	22 16	0 37	15 49	16 2	1 16	12 5
15	1 42	21 29	21 13	1 58	22 2	21 46	0 36	16 15	16 28	1 16	12 3
17	2 16	20 58	20 42	1 58	21 30	21 14	0 35	16 41	16 54	1 15	12 2
19	2 49	20 27	20 13	1 58	20 57	20 39	0 34	17 6	17 18	1 15	12 1
21	3 19	20 0	19 47	1 57	20 21	20 2	0 32	17 30	17 42	1 14	12 0
23	3 46	19 35	19 24	1 56	19 43	19 23	0 31	17 54	18 6	1 14	11 59
25	4 9	19 15	19 6	1 55	19 3	18 43	0 30	18 17	18 28	1 13	11 59
27	4 26	18 59	18 53	1 53	18 22	18 0	0 28	18 39	18 50	1 13	11 59
29	4 38	18 48	18 N 45	1 50	17 38	17 N16	0 27	19 1	19 N 11	1 12	11 59
31	4 S43	18 N43		1 N 48	16 N53		0 S 26	19 N21		1 N 12	11 S 59

FIRST QUARTER-June16, 7h.57m. pm. (25°♍26′)

FULL MOON-June23,11h.33m. am. (1°♑47′)

D M	☿ Long.	♀ Long.	♂ Long.	♃ Long.	♄ Long.	♅ Long.	♆ Long.	♇ Long.	☉	☿	♀	♂	♃	♄	♅	♆	♇
	° ′	° ′	° ′	° ′	° ′	° ′	° ′	° ′									
1	3♋41	13♋40	6♉24	6♏ 8	12♓ 1	25♑57	23♑ 0	26♏17	□		△			☌	∠		
2	4 28	14 52	7 8	6R 3	12 3	25R 55	22R 59	26R 16				∠	⚼		✱	✱	△
3	5 12	16 3	7 53	5 58	12 5	25 54	22 58	26 14	✱	□		⊻		⊻			⚼
4	5 51	17 14	8 37	5 53	12 7	25 52	22 57	26 13			□				□	□	
5	6 25	18 25	9 22	5 49	12 9	25 51	22 55	26 11	∠	✱			☍	∠			
6	6 56	19 36	10 6	5 44	12 10	25 49	22 54	26 10	⊻			☌		✱			
7	7 22	20 47	10 51	5 40	12 12	25 47	22 53	26 8		∠	✱				△	△	☍
8	7 44	21 58	11 35	5 36	12 14	25 46	22 52	26 7		⊻	∠	⊻		□	⚼	⚼	
9	8 1	23 9	12 19	5 32	12 15	25 44	22 50	26 5	☌		⊻		⚼				
10	8 13	24 20	13 3	5 28	12 16	25 42	22 49	26 4		☌		∠	△				
11	8 21	25 31	13 47	5 24	12 17	25 40	22 48	26 2	⊻			✱		△			⚼
12	8 25	26 42	14 31	5 21	12 19	25 39	22 47	26 1			☌			⚼	☍	☍	△
13	8R 23	27 52	15 15	5 17	12 20	25 37	22 45	25 59	∠	⊻		□	□				
14	8 18	29♋ 3	15 59	5 14	12 20	25 35	22 44	25 58	✱	∠	⊻						□
15	8 8	0♌14	16 43	5 11	12 21	25 33	22 43	25 56		✱			✱	☍	⚼	⚼	
16	7 54	1 24	17 27	5 8	12 22	25 31	22 41	25 55	□		∠	△	∠		△	△	✱
17	7 36	2 34	18 10	5 5	12 23	25 29	22 40	25 54		□	✱	⚼	⊻				∠
18	7 14	3 45	18 54	5 3	12 23	25 27	22 38	25 52							□	□	⊻
19	6 49	4 55	19 38	5 0	12 24	25 25	22 37	25 51	△	△	□		☌	⚼			
20	6 21	6 5	20 21	4 58	12 24	25 23	22 36	25 49	⚼	⚼		☍		△	✱	✱	
21	5 51	7 15	21 5	4 56	12 24	25 21	22 34	25 48			△		⊻			∠	☌
22	5 18	8 25	21 48	4 54	12 24	25 19	22 33	25 47			⚼		∠	□	∠	⊻	
23	4 44	9 35	22 31	4 53	12R 24	25 17	22 31	25 46	☍	☍		⚼	✱		⊻		⊻
24	4 9	10 44	23 15	4 51	12 24	25 15	22 30	25 44						✱		☌	∠
25	3 34	11 54	23 58	4 50	12 24	25 12	22 28	25 43				△	□	∠	☌		✱
26	3 0	13 4	24 41	4 49	12 24	25 10	22 27	25 42	⚼	⚼	☍			⊻			
27	2 26	14 13	25 24	4 48	12 23	25 8	22 25	25 41		△		□			⊻	⊻	□
28	1 53	15 23	26 7	4 47	12 23	25 6	22 24	25 40	△				△	☌	∠	∠	
29	1 23	16 32	26 50	4 47	12 22	25 3	22 22	25 39				✱	⚼		✱	✱	△
30	0♋55	17♌41	27♉33	4♏46	12♓22	25♑ 1	22♑20	25♏37	□	□	⚼						⚼

D M	Saturn Lat.	Saturn Dec.	Uranus Lat.	Uranus Dec.	Neptune Lat.	Neptune Dec.	Pluto Lat.	Pluto Dec.
	° ′	° ′	° ′	° ′	° ′	° ′	° ′	° ′
1	1S41	8S37	0S31	21S28	0N37	20S52	14N23	5S19
3	1 41	8 35	0 31	21 28	0 37	20 52	14 23	5 19
5	1 42	8 34	0 31	21 29	0 37	20 53	14 22	5 18
7	1 42	8 34	0 31	21 30	0 37	20 53	14 22	5 18
9	1 43	8 33	0 31	21 30	0 37	20 53	14 21	5 18
11	1 43	8 32	0 31	21 31	0 37	20 54	14 21	5 18
13	1 44	8 32	0 31	21 32	0 37	20 54	14 20	5 18
15	1 44	8 32	0 31	21 32	0 37	20 55	14 19	5 18
17	1 45	8 32	0 31	21 33	0 37	20 55	14 19	5 18
19	1 45	8 32	0 31	21 34	0 37	20 56	14 18	5 18
21	1 46	8 32	0 31	21 35	0 37	20 56	14 18	5 18
23	1 46	8 33	0 31	21 36	0 37	20 57	14 17	5 18
25	1 47	8 33	0 31	21 36	0 37	20 57	14 16	5 18
27	1 47	8 34	0 31	21 37	0 37	20 58	14 15	5 18
29	1 48	8 35	0 31	21 38	0 37	20 58	14 15	5 19
31	1S48	8S36	0S31	21S39	0N37	20S59	14N14	5S19

1 ☉⚼♅. ♂☍♃.
2 ☉±♃. ☉□♄.
4 ☿△♃.
6 ☿P♀.
7 ☉±♆.
9 ☉⊥♂. ♀☍♆. ♂✱♄.
10 ☉±♅. ☉P☿.
11 ☉⚼♃. ♀☍♅. ♀△♇. ☉P♀.
12 ♀Q♂. ☿Stat.
13 ♀⚼♄.
14 ☉▽♆.
15 ☉⊥♀. ☿P♅.
16 ☉▽♅.
17 ☉▽♇. ☿P♆. ♀P♅.
19 ♀□♃. ♀P♆.
20 ☿⊻♀. ♀±♄.
21 ☿∠♂.
23 ☉±♇. ☿△♃. ♂△♆. ♄Stat.
24 ☿⊥♀. ☿P♀.
25 ☉P☿. ♀▽♄.
26 ☉△♃. ♂Q♄. ♀P♂.
27 ♂△♅. ♂☍♇.
28 ☿⊥♂. ☿±♇. ☿P♂.
29 ☿∠♀.

LAST QUARTER-June 1, 4h. 2m. am. (10°♓27′) & June30, 7h.31m. pm. (8°♈46′)

14					JULY	1994			[RAPHAEL'S	
D M	D W	Sidereal Time	⊙ Long.	⊙ Dec.	☽ Long.	☽ Lat.	☽ Dec.	☽ Node	Midnight ☽ Long.	☽ Dec.
		H. M. S.	° ′ ″	° ′	° ′ ″	° ′	° ′	° ′	° ′ ″	° ′
1	F	6 37 14	9♋25 27	23 N 6	16♈58 50	3 N 2	9 N28	21 ♏ 29	22 ♈ 54 55	11 N18
2	S	6 41 11	10 22 40	23 2	28 49 38	2 6	13 1	21 26	4 ♉ 43 37	14 37
3	Su	6 45 7	11 19 53	22 57	10♉37 28	1 6	16 3	21 23	16 31 50	17 19
4	M	6 49 4	12 17 6	22 52	22 27 15	0 N 2	18 25	21 19	28 24 17	19 19
5	T	6 53 0	13 14 19	22 47	4♊28 24	1 S 2	20 0	21 16	10♊25 3	20 28
6	W	6 56 57	14 11 32	22 41	16 29 37	2 4	20 42	21 13	22 37 25	20 41
7	Th	7 0 54	15 8 46	22 35	28 48 42	3 1	20 25	21 10	5♋ 3 41	19 54
8	F	7 4 50	16 6 0	22 28	11♋22 27	3 51	19 7	21 7	17 45 4	18 6
9	S	7 8 47	17 3 14	22 21	24 11 32	4 29	16 51	21 3	0♌41 47	15 23
10	Su	7 12 43	18 0 28	22 14	7♌15 40	4 55	13 42	21 0	13 53 4	11 50
11	M	7 16 40	18 57 42	22 6	20 33 46	5 5	9 48	20 57	27 17 34	7 39
12	T	7 20 36	19 54 56	21 58	4♍ 4 15	4 59	5 22	20 54	10♍53 36	3 N 1
13	W	7 24 33	20 52 10	21 49	17 45 26	4 35	0 N37	20 51	24 39 33	1 S49
14	Th	7 28 29	21 49 24	21 40	1♎35 48	3 55	4 S14	20 48	8♎34 3	6 37
15	F	7 32 26	22 46 38	21 31	15 34 10	3 1	8 55	20 44	22 36 3	11 6
16	S	7 36 23	23 43 52	21 21	29 39 34	1 56	13 9	20 41	6♏44 38	15 1
17	Su	7 40 19	24 41 6	21 11	13♏51 3	0 S42	16 40	20 38	20 58 40	18 4
18	M	7 44 16	25 38 21	21 1	28 7 13	0 N34	19 12	20 35	5♐16 25	20 1
19	T	7 48 12	26 35 35	20 50	12♐25 53	1 48	20 30	20 32	19 35 10	20 40
20	W	7 52 9	27 32 50	20 39	26 43 47	2 55	20 29	20 29	3♑51 10	19 59
21	Th	7 56 5	28 30 5	20 28	10♑56 42	3 50	19 10	20 25	17 59 48	18 3
22	F	8 0 2	29♋27 21	20 16	24 59 51	4 31	16 41	20 22	1♒56 16	15 5
23	S	8 3 58	0♌24 37	20 4	8♒48 31	4 56	13 18	20 19	15 36 11	11 22
24	Su	8 7 55	1 21 54	19 51	22 18 53	5 2	9 18	20 16	28 56 25	7 9
25	M	8 11 52	2 19 11	19 39	5♓28 38	4 53	4 57	20 13	11♓55 32	2 S44
26	T	8 15 48	3 16 29	19 25	18 17 14	4 29	0 S30	20 9	24 33 57	1 N42
27	W	8 19 45	4 13 48	19 12	0♈46 0	3 52	3 N51	20 6	6♈53 48	5 57
28	Th	8 23 41	5 11 8	18 58	12 57 49	3 6	7 28	20 3	18 58 36	9 53
29	F	8 27 38	6 8 29	18 44	24 56 45	2 12	11 42	20 0	0 ♉ 52 55	13 23
30	S	8 31 34	7 5 51	18 30	6♉47 44	1 13	14 55	19 57	12 41 55	16 19
31	Su	8 35 31	8♌ 3 14	18 N15	18♉36 8	0 N10	17 N32	19 ♏ 54	24♉31 4	18 N34

D M	Mercury Lat	Mercury Dec		Venus Lat	Venus Dec		Mars Lat	Mars Dec		Jupiter Lat	Jupiter Dec
	° ′	° ′	° ′	° ′	° ′	° ′	° ′	° ′	° ′	° ′	° ′
1	4 S 43	18 N43	18 N 43	1 N 48	16 N53	16 N30	0 S 26	19 N21	19 N 31	1 N 12	11 S 59
3	4 43	18 44	18 46	1 45	16 6	15 42	0 24	19 41	19 51	1 11	12 0
5	4 36	18 50	18 55	1 41	15 18	14 53	0 23	20 1	20 10	1 11	12 2
7	4 25	19 1	19 9	1 37	14 28	14 13	0 21	20 19	20 28	1 10	12 2
9	4 9	19 17	19 26	1 33	13 38	13 12	0 20	20 37	20 45	1 9	12 3
11	3 50	19 37	19 47	1 28	12 45	12 19	0 18	20 53	21 2	1 9	12 4
13	3 27	19 59	20 10	1 23	11 52	11 25	0 17	21 9	21 17	1 8	12 6
15	3 0	20 22	20 34	1 17	10 58	10 30	0 15	21 25	21 32	1 8	12 8
17	2 36	20 46	20 58	1 12	10 3	9 35	0 14	21 41	21 46	1 7	12 10
19	2 8	21 9	21 20	1 5	9 6	8 38	0 12	21 53	21 59	1 7	12 13
21	1 40	21 30	21 39	0 58	8 10	7 41	0 11	22 5	22 11	1 6	12 15
23	1 11	21 46	21 53	0 51	7 12	6 43	0 9	22 17	22 23	1 6	12 18
25	0 43	21 58	22 0	0 44	6 14	5 45	0 8	22 28	22 34	1 5	12 21
27	0 S 17	22 1	22 0	0 36	5 16	4 46	0 6	22 40	22 44	1 5	12 24
29	0 N 8	21 57	21 N 51	0 27	4 17	3 N47	0 4	22 48	22 N 53	1 4	12 28
31	0 N31	21 N43		0 N 18	3 N17		0 S 3	22 N57		1 N 4	12 S 32

FULL MOON-July22, 8h.16m. pm. (29°♑47′)

D M	☿ Long.	♀ Long.	♂ Long.	♃ Long.	♄ Long.	♅ Long.	♆ Long.	♇ Long.	☉	☿	♀	♂	♃	♄	♅	♆	♇
	° ′	° ′	° ′	° ′	° ′	° ′	° ′	° ′									
1	0♋30	18♌50	28♉16	4♏46	12♓21	24♑59	22♑19	25♏36			△	∠		⚺		□	
2	0♋ 9	19 59	28 59	4D 46	12R 20	24R 57	22R 17	25R 35		⚹		⚺		∠	□		
3	29♊51	21 8	29♉41	4 46	12 19	24 54	22 16	25 34	⚹	∠			☍	⚹			
4	29R 38	22 17	0♊24	4 47	12 18	24 52	22 14	25 33	∠		□				△	△	☍
5	29 29	23 26	1 7	4 47	12 17	24 50	22 13	25 32		⚺		☌			⚼	⚼	
6	29 25	24 34	1 49	4 48	12 15	24 47	22 11	25 31	⚺				⚼	□			
7	29D 26	25 43	2 31	4 49	12 14	24 45	22 9	25 30		☌	⚹	⚺	△				
8	29 32	26 51	3 14	4 50	12 13	24 43	22 8	25 29	☌		∠			△			⚼
9	29 43	27 59	3 56	4 51	12 11	24 40	22 6	25 29		⚺	⚺	∠		⚼	☍	☍	△
10	29♊59	29♌ 7	4 38	4 52	12 9	24 38	22 5	25 28				⚹	□				
11	0♋21	0♍15	5 21	4 54	12 8	24 35	22 3	25 27	⚺	∠							□
12	0 48	1 23	6 3	4 56	12 6	24 33	22 1	25 26	∠	⚹	☌	□	⚹		⚼	⚼	
13	1 20	2 31	6 45	4 58	12 4	24 31	22 0	25 25	⚹				∠	☍	△	△	
14	1 57	3 39	7 27	5 0	12 2	24 28	21 58	25 25		□	⚺	△	⚺				⚹
15	2 39	4 46	8 8	5 2	12 0	24 26	21 56	25 24			∠					□	∠
16	3 27	5 54	8 50	5 5	11 58	24 23	21 55	25 23	□	△	⚹	⚼	☌	⚼	□		⚺
17	4 19	7 1	9 32	5 7	11 55	24 21	21 53	25 23		⚼				△			
18	5 17	8 8	10 14	5 10	11 53	24 19	21 52	25 22	△				⚺		⚹	⚹	☌
19	6 19	9 15	10 55	5 13	11 51	24 16	21 50	25 22	⚼		□	☍		□	∠	∠	
20	7 27	10 22	11 37	5 16	11 48	24 14	21 48	25 21					∠		⚺	⚺	⚺
21	8 39	11 28	12 18	5 19	11 45	24 11	21 47	25 20		☍	△		⚹	⚹			∠
22	9 56	12 35	12 59	5 23	11 43	24 9	21 45	25 20	☍		⚼	⚼		∠	☌	☌	⚹
23	11 17	13 41	13 41	5 27	11 40	24 7	21 44	25 20				△	□	⚺			
24	12 44	14 47	14 22	5 30	11 37	24 4	21 42	25 19		⚼					⚺	⚺	□
25	14 14	15 53	15 3	5 34	11 34	24 2	21 40	25 19					△	☌	∠	∠	
26	15 49	16 59	15 44	5 39	11 31	23 59	21 39	25 18	⚼	△	☍	□	⚼		⚹	⚹	
27	17 27	18 4	16 25	5 43	11 28	23 57	21 37	25 18	△								△
28	19 10	19 10	17 6	5 47	11 25	23 55	21 36	25 18				⚹		⚺			⚼
29	20 56	20 15	17 47	5 52	11 22	23 52	21 34	25 17		□				∠	□	□	
30	22 45	21 20	18 28	5 57	11 18	23 50	21 32	25 17	□		⚼	∠	☍	⚹			
31	24♋37	22♍25	19♊ 8	6♏ 2	11♓15	23♑48	21♑31	25♏17			△	⚺			△	△	

D M	Saturn Lat.	Saturn Dec.	Uranus Lat.	Uranus Dec.	Neptune Lat.	Neptune Dec.	Pluto Lat.	Pluto Dec.
	° ′	° ′	° ′	° ′	° ′	° ′	° ′	° ′
1	1S48	8S36	0S31	21S39	0N37	20S59	14N14	5S19
3	1 49	8 37	0 31	21 40	0 37	20 59	14 13	5 19
5	1 49	8 38	0 32	21 41	0 37	21 0	14 12	5 20
7	1 50	8 39	0 32	21 42	0 37	21 0	14 11	5 20
9	1 50	8 41	0 32	21 42	0 37	21 1	14 10	5 21
11	1 50	8 43	0 32	21 43	0 37	21 1	14 9	5 21
13	1 51	8 45	0 32	21 44	0 37	21 2	14 8	5 22
15	1 51	8 47	0 32	21 45	0 37	21 2	14 7	5 22
17	1 52	8 49	0 32	21 46	0 37	21 3	14 6	5 23
19	1 52	8 51	0 32	21 47	0 37	21 3	14 6	5 24
21	1 53	8 53	0 32	21 48	0 37	21 4	14 5	5 24
23	1 53	8 56	0 32	21 48	0 37	21 5	14 4	5 25
25	1 53	8 58	0 32	21 49	0 37	21 5	14 2	5 26
27	1 54	9 1	0 32	21 50	0 37	21 6	14 1	5 27
29	1 54	9 4	0 32	21 51	0 37	21 6	14 0	5 28
31	1S55	9S 7	0S32	21S52	0N37	21S 7	13N59	5S29

2 ☉⚼♇. ♃Stat.
3 ☿⚺♂.
4 ☉△♄. ♀Q♃. ♀∇♆.
6 ♀∇♅. ☿Stat.
7 ♀□♇.
9 ♀±♆.
10 ♂∇♃.
11 ☿⚹♀. ♀±♅.
12 ♀P♃. ♂P♆.
13 ☿±♇. ♂⚼♆.
14 ☉☍♆. ☉P♅.
15 ♀⚹♃. ☉P♂.
16 ☉∠♂.
17 ☉☍♅. ♀⚼♆. ♂⚼♅.
18 ☉△♇. ☿△♃. ☉P☿. ☉P♆. ☿P♆.
♂P♅.
19 ☉⚼♄. ♀⚼♅. ♂±♃.
20 ♂□♄. ♀P♄.
21 ♀☍♄.
22 ☿⚼♇.
23 ☿△♄. ♀□♂. ♀Q♇. ☿P♅.
26 ☿⚺♂. ♂±♆.
27 ♀P♇.
28 ☉±♄. ☿⚹♀.
29 ☉□♃. ☿☍♆. ♂±♅.
30 ♀∠♃. ♀△♆. ☿P♅.
31 ☿⊥♂. ☿☍♅. ☿△♇.

LAST QUARTER-July30, 0h.40m. pm. (7°♉ 7′)

NEW MOON-Aug. 7, 8h.45m. am. (14° ♌ 38′)

D M	D W	Sidereal Time	⊙ Long.	⊙ Dec.	☽ Long.	☽ Lat.	☽ Dec.	☽ Node	Midnight ☽ Long.	☽ Dec.
		H. M. S.	° ′ ″	° ′	° ′ ″	° ′	° ′	° ′	° ′ ″	° ′
1	M	8 39 27	9 ♌ 0 38	18 N 0	0 ♊ 27 23	0 S 52	19 N24	19 ♏ 50	6 ♊ 25 44	20 N 1
2	T	8 43 24	9 58 3	17 45	12 26 43	1 53	20 25	19 47	18 30 53	20 34
3	W	8 47 21	10 55 30	17 29	24 38 45	2 50	20 30	19 44	0 ♋ 50 45	20 10
4	Th	8 51 17	11 52 57	17 14	7 ♋ 7 14	3 40	19 35	19 41	13 28 27	18 45
5	F	8 55 14	12 50 26	16 57	19 54 35	4 20	17 40	19 38	26 25 41	16 21
6	S	8 59 10	13 47 56	16 41	3 ♌ 1 42	4 48	14 49	19 35	9 ♌ 42 29	13 4
7	Su	9 3 7	14 45 27	16 24	16 27 45	5 0	11 7	19 31	23 17 11	9 2
8	M	9 7 3	15 42 58	16 7	0 ♍ 10 21	4 56	6 48	19 28	7 ♍ 6 45	4 N27
9	T	9 11 0	16 40 31	15 50	14 5 53	4 34	2 N 3	19 25	21 7 12	0 S 24
10	W	9 14 56	17 38 5	15 33	28 10 12	3 55	2 S 52	19 22	5 ♎ 14 23	5 18
11	Th	9 18 53	18 35 39	15 15	12 ♎ 19 19	3 2	7 39	19 19	19 24 35	9 55
12	F	9 22 50	19 33 15	14 57	26 29 54	1 57	12 2	19 15	3 ♏ 35 0	13 59
13	S	9 26 46	20 30 51	14 39	10 ♏ 39 39	0 S 45	15 44	19 12	17 43 44	17 14
14	Su	9 30 43	21 28 28	14 21	24 47 6	0 N30	18 29	19 9	1 ♐ 49 40	19 26
15	M	9 34 39	22 26 7	14 2	8 ♐ 51 19	1 42	20 5	19 6	15 51 58	20 26
16	T	9 38 36	23 23 46	13 43	22 51 28	2 48	20 27	19 3	29 49 39	20 9
17	W	9 42 32	24 21 26	13 24	6 ♑ 46 20	3 44	19 33	19 0	13 ♑ 41 15	18 39
18	Th	9 46 29	25 19 8	13 5	20 34 8	4 25	17 29	18 56	27 24 39	16 5
19	F	9 50 25	26 16 50	12 45	4 ♒ 12 29	4 51	14 29	18 53	10 ♒ 57 19	12 42
20	S	9 54 22	27 14 34	12 26	17 38 47	5 1	10 46	18 50	24 16 38	8 43
21	Su	9 58 19	28 12 19	12 6	0 ♓ 50 35	4 54	6 35	18 47	7 ♓ 20 26	4 S 24
22	M	10 2 15	29 ♌ 10 5	11 46	13 46 6	4 32	2 S 12	18 44	20 7 30	0 0
23	T	10 6 12	0 ♍ 7 53	11 26	26 24 41	3 57	2 N12	18 41	2 ♈ 37 46	4 N20
24	W	10 10 8	1 5 42	11 5	8 ♈ 46 59	3 11	6 24	18 37	14 52 35	8 24
25	Th	10 14 5	2 3 33	10 44	20 54 57	2 17	10 17	18 34	26 54 32	12 3
26	F	10 18 1	3 1 26	10 24	2 ♉ 51 48	1 18	13 41	18 31	8 ♉ 47 20	15 10
27	S	10 21 58	3 59 20	10 3	14 41 42	0 N16	16 30	18 28	20 35 32	17 39
28	Su	10 25 54	4 57 17	9 42	26 29 31	0 S 47	18 37	18 25	2 ♊ 24 19	19 22
29	M	10 29 51	5 55 15	9 20	8 ♊ 20 37	1 48	19 55	18 21	14 19 7	20 15
30	T	10 33 48	6 53 15	8 59	20 20 28	2 45	20 21	18 18	26 25 19	20 12
31	W	10 37 44	7 ♍ 51 17	8 N37	2 ♋ 34 18	3 S 35	19 N49	18 ♏ 15	8 ♋ 47 56	19 N12

D M	Mercury Lat.	Mercury Dec.		Venus Lat.	Venus Dec.		Mars Lat.	Mars Dec.		Jupiter Lat.	Jupiter Dec.
	° ′	° ′	° ′	° ′	° ′	° ′	° ′	° ′	° ′	° ′	° ′
1	0 N42	21 N32	21 N 18	0 N 14	2 N48	2 N18	0 S 2	23 N 1	23 N 5	1 N 3	12 S 34
3	1 0	21 2	20 43	0 N 5	1 48	1 18	0 0	23 8	23 12	1 3	12 37
5	1 16	20 21	19 57	0 S 5	0 N48	0 N19	0 N 1	23 15	23 18	1 3	12 42
7	1 28	19 31	19 2	0 15	0 S 11	0 S 41	0 3	23 21	23 24	1 2	12 46
9	1 37	18 31	17 58	0 26	1 11	1 41	0 5	23 26	23 28	1 2	12 50
11	1 43	17 24	16 47	0 36	2 10	2 40	0 7	23 30	23 32	1 1	12 55
13	1 46	16 10	15 30	0 48	3 10	3 39	0 8	23 34	23 35	1 1	13 0
15	1 45	14 50	14 8	0 59	4 9	4 38	0 10	23 36	23 37	1 0	13 5
17	1 43	13 26	12 43	1 11	5 7	5 37	0 12	23 39	23 39	1 0	13 10
19	1 38	11 59	11 15	1 23	6 6	6 34	0 14	23 39	23 40	0 59	13 15
21	1 31	10 30	9 45	1 35	7 3	7 32	0 16	23 40	23 40	0 59	13 21
23	1 22	8 59	8 13	1 47	8 0	8 28	0 17	23 39	23 39	0 58	13 26
25	1 12	7 27	6 41	2 0	8 56	9 24	0 19	23 38	23 37	0 58	13 32
27	1 5	5 55	5 10	2 13	9 52	10 19	0 21	23 36	23 35	0 58	13 38
29	0 48	4 24	3 N 38	2 27	10 46	11 S 13	0 23	23 34	23 N 32	0 57	13 44
31	0 N34	2 N53		2 S 40	11 S 40		0 N 25	23 N31		0 N 57	13 S 50

FIRST QUARTER-Aug.14, 5h.57m. am. (21° ♏ 14′)

FULL MOON-Aug.21, 6h.47m. am. (28°♒ 0′)

D M	☿ Long.	♀ Long.	♂ Long.	♃ Long.	♄ Long.	♅ Long.	♆ Long.	♇ Long.	Lunar Aspects ☉	☿	♀	♂	♃	♄	♅	♆	♇
	° ′	° ′	° ′	° ′	° ′	° ′	° ′	° ′									
1	26♋32	23♍30	19♊49	6♏ 7	11♓12	23♑45	21♑29	25♏17		⚹							☍
2	28♋30	24 34	20 29	6 12	11R 8	23R 43	21R 28	25R 17	⚹	∠				□	⚼	⚼	
3	0♌29	25 38	21 10	6 17	11 5	23 41	21 26	25 17	∠		□	☌	⚼				
4	2 30	26 42	21 50	6 23	11 1	23 39	21 25	25 17	⚺	⚺			△	△			⚼
5	4 33	27 46	22 30	6 28	10 57	23 36	21 23	25 17				⚺		⚼	☍	☍	△
6	6 36	28 50	23 11	6 34	10 53	23 34	21 22	25D 17		☌	⚹	∠	□				
7	8 40	29♍53	23 51	6 40	10 50	23 32	21 20	25 17	☌		∠						
8	10 44	0♎56	24 31	6 46	10 46	23 30	21 19	25 17			⚺	⚹	⚹			⚼	□
9	12 48	1 59	25 11	6 53	10 42	23 28	21 18	25 17	⚺	⚺				☍	⚼		
10	14 52	3 2	25 51	6 59	10 38	23 25	21 16	25 17	∠	∠	☌	□	∠		△	△	⚹
11	16 56	4 4	26 30	7 6	10 34	23 23	21 15	25 17	⚹	⚹			⚺				∠
12	18 59	5 6	27 10	7 12	10 30	23 21	21 13	25 17				△		⚼	□	□	⚺
13	21 1	6 8	27 50	7 19	10 26	23 19	21 12	25 18			⚺	⚼	☌	△			
14	23 2	7 10	28 29	7 26	10 21	23 17	21 11	25 18	□	□	∠				⚹	⚹	☌
15	25 2	8 11	29 9	7 33	10 17	23 15	21 9	25 18			⚹		⚺	□	∠	∠	
16	27 0	9 12	29♊48	7 40	10 13	23 13	21 8	25 19	△	△			∠		⚺	⚺	⚺
17	28♌58	10 12	0♋27	7 48	10 9	23 11	21 7	25 19	⚼		□	☍	⚹	⚹			∠
18	0♍54	11 12	1 7	7 55	10 4	23 9	21 5	25 19		⚼				∠	☌	☌	⚹
19	2 49	12 12	1 46	8 3	10 0	23 7	21 4	25 20					□	⚺			
20	4 43	13 12	2 25	8 11	9 56	23 6	21 3	25 20			△	⚼			⚺	⚺	
21	6 35	14 11	3 4	8 19	9 51	23 4	21 2	25 21	☍		⚼	△				∠	□
22	8 26	15 10	3 42	8 27	9 47	23 2	21 0	25 21		☍			△	☌	∠		
23	10 16	16 8	4 21	8 35	9 42	23 0	20 59	25 22					⚼		⚹	⚹	△
24	12 4	17 6	5 0	8 43	9 38	22 58	20 58	25 23				□		⚺			⚼
25	13 51	18 4	5 38	8 51	9 33	22 57	20 57	25 23	⚼		☍			∠	□	□	
26	15 36	19 1	6 17	9 0	9 29	22 55	20 56	25 24	△	⚼		⚹					
27	17 21	19 58	6 55	9 8	9 24	22 53	20 55	25 25		△			☍	⚹			
28	19 3	20 54	7 34	9 17	9 20	22 52	20 54	25 25				∠			△	△	☍
29	20 45	21 50	8 12	9 26	9 15	22 50	20 53	25 26	□		⚼	⚺		□	⚼	⚼	
30	22 25	22 45	8 50	9 35	9 11	22 49	20 52	25 27		□	△		⚼				
31	24♍ 4	23♎40	9♋28	9♏44	9♓ 6	22♑47	20♑51	25♏28	⚹								

D M	Saturn Lat.	Saturn Dec.	Uranus Lat.	Uranus Dec.	Neptune Lat.	Neptune Dec.	Pluto Lat.	Pluto Dec.
	° ′	° ′	° ′	° ′	° ′	° ′	° ′	° ′
1	1S55	9S 8	0S32	21S52	0N37	21S 7	13N59	5S29
3	1 55	9 11	0 32	21 53	0 37	21 7	13 58	5 30
5	1 55	9 14	0 32	21 54	0 37	21 8	13 57	5 31
7	1 56	9 17	0 32	21 54	0 37	21 8	13 56	5 32
9	1 56	9 21	0 32	21 55	0 37	21 9	13 55	5 33
11	1 56	9 24	0 32	21 56	0 37	21 9	13 53	5 34
13	1 57	9 27	0 32	21 57	0 37	21 10	13 52	5 36
15	1 57	9 31	0 32	21 57	0 37	21 10	13 51	5 37
17	1 57	9 34	0 32	21 58	0 37	21 11	13 50	5 38
19	1 57	9 38	0 32	21 59	0 37	21 11	13 49	5 39
21	1 58	9 41	0 32	21 59	0 37	21 12	13 48	5 40
23	1 58	9 45	0 32	22 0	0 36	21 12	13 47	5 42
25	1 58	9 48	0 32	22 0	0 36	21 12	13 46	5 43
27	1 58	9 52	0 32	22 1	0 36	21 13	13 45	5 44
29	1 58	9 56	0 32	22 1	0 36	21 13	13 44	5 46
31	1S58	9S59	0S31	22S 2	0N36	21S13	13N43	5S47

Mutual Aspects

1 ☿⚼♄. ♀△♅.
3 ☉▽♄. ♀⚹♇. ♂⚼♃. ♂▽♆. ☿P♆.
5 ☿±♄. ♇Stat.
6 ☉∠♀. ☿□♃.
7 ☿∠♂. ♂▽♅.
8 ☿▽♄. ♀⊥♃.
9 ♂▽♇.
13 ☉☌☿. ☿∠♀. ☿▽♆.
14 ☉▽♆. ☿▽♅. ♀⚺♃.
15 ☿Q♃. ☿□♇.
16 ☉▽♅. ☿±♆.
17 ☿±♅. ♀▽♄. ♀∠♇. ☉P☿. ☿P♃.
18 ☉□♇. ☿⚹♂. ♂±♇. ☉P♃. ♀P♇.
19 ☉Q♃.
20 ☉±♆.
21 ☿⚼♆.
22 ☉±♅. ☿⚹♃. ☿⚼♅. ☿P♄.
23 ☿⊥♀. ☿☍♄. ♀±♄.
24 ☿P♀.
25 ☿Q♇.
26 ♀⊥♇. ♃Q♆.
27 ☉P♀. ☉P♄. ☿P♇. ♀P♄.
28 ☿Q♂. ♀□♆. ♃△♄.
29 ☉⚼♆. ☿△♆.
30 ☿⚺♀. ☿△♅. ♀□♅. ♂△♄.
31 ☉⚼♅. ☿∠♃. ♀⚼♄.

LAST QUARTER-Aug.29, 6h.41m. am. (5°♊42′)

18					SEPTEMBER		1994			[RAPHAEL'S	
D	D	Sidereal	☉	☉	☽	☽	☽	☽		Midnight	
M	W	Time	Long.	Dec.	Long.	Lat.	Dec.	Node	☽ Long.		☽ Dec.

		H. M. S.	° ′ ″	° ′	° ′ ″	° ′	° ′	° ′	° ′ ″	° ′
1	Th	10 41 41	8♍49 20	8 N16	15♋ 6 43	4 S17	18 N20	18 ♏ 12	21 ♋ 31 3	17 N13
2	F	10 45 37	9 47 26	7 54	28 1 12	4 47	15 52	18 9	4 ♌ 37 22	14 19
3	S	10 49 34	10 45 34	7 32	11 ♌ 19 35	5 2	12 32	18 6	18 7 45	10 35
4	Su	10 53 30	11 43 43	7 10	25 1 36	5 1	8 27	18 2	2 ♍ 0 46	6 11
5	M	10 57 27	12 41 54	6 48	9♍ 4 43	4 41	3 N49	17 59	16 12 47	1 N22

6	T	11 1 23	13 40 7	6 25	23 24 16	4 4	1 S 7	17 56	0 ♎ 38 21	3 S37
7	W	11 5 20	14 38 21	6 3	7 ♎ 54 12	3 11	6 4	17 53	15 11 2	8 26
8	Th	11 9 17	15 36 37	5 40	22 28 2	2 5	10 41	17 50	29 44 30	12 46
9	F	11 13 13	16 34 55	5 18	6 ♏ 59 49	0 S55	14 39	17 47	14 ♏ 13 25	16 18
10	S	11 17 10	17 33 14	4 55	21 24 53	0 N26	17 41	17 43	28 33 52	18 48

11	Su	11 21 6	18 31 35	4 32	5 ♐ 40 10	1 41	19 36	17 40	12 ♐ 43 35	20 5
12	M	11 25 3	19 29 57	4 9	19 44 2	2 48	20 15	17 37	26 41 28	20 6
13	T	11 28 59	20 28 21	3 47	3 ♑35 52	3 45	19 38	17 34	10 ♑ 27 15	18 54
14	W	11 32 56	21 26 47	3 24	17 15 36	4 28	17 54	17 31	24 0 56	16 39
15	Th	11 36 52	22 25 14	3 0	0 ♒43 15	4 55	15 11	17 27	7 ♒ 22 32	13 33

16	F	11 40 49	23 23 42	2 37	13 58 45	5 6	11 44	17 24	20 31 51	9 49
17	S	11 44 46	24 22 13	2 14	27 1 47	5 1	7 47	17 21	3 ♓ 28 31	5 41
18	Su	11 48 42	25 20 45	1 51	9 ♓ 51 59	4 41	3 S32	17 18	16 12 11	1 S22
19	M	11 52 39	26 19 18	1 28	22 29 6	4 7	0 N48	17 15	28 42 47	2 N56
20	T	11 56 35	27 17 54	1 4	4 ♈53 19	3 21	5 1	17 12	11 ♈ 0 43	7 3

21	W	12 0 32	28 16 32	0 41	17 5 16	2 28	8 59	17 8	23 7 8	10 49
22	Th	12 4 28	29♍15 12	0 N18	29 6 35	1 28	12 31	17 5	5 ♉ 3 58	14 6
23	F	12 8 25	0 ♎13 54	0 S 6	10 ♉ 59 38	0 N24	15 31	17 2	16 54 1	16 46
24	S	12 12 21	1 12 38	0 29	22 47 35	0 S40	17 50	16 59	28 40 52	18 43
25	Su	12 16 18	2 11 24	0 52	4 ♊ 34 25	1 42	19 23	16 56	10 ♊ 28 49	19 51

26	M	12 20 15	3 10 13	1 16	16 24 42	2 40	20 5	16 52	22 22 41	20 6
27	T	12 24 11	4 9 3	1 39	28 23 25	3 32	19 54	16 49	4 ♋ 27 33	19 27
28	W	12 28 8	5 7 56	2 2	10 ♋35 44	4 16	18 46	16 46	16 48 33	17 52
29	Th	12 32 4	6 6 52	2 26	23 6 35	4 48	16 43	16 43	29 30 21	15 22
30	F	12 36 1	7 ♎ 5 49	2 S49	6 ♌ 0 16	5 S 7	13 N48	16 ♏ 40	12 ♌ 36 41	12 N 2

D		Mercury		Venus		Mars		Jupiter	
M	Lat.	Dec.	Lat.	Dec.	Lat.	Dec.	Lat.	Dec.

	° ′	° ′		° ′	° ′		° ′	° ′		° ′	° ′		° ′	° ′
1	0 N27	2 N 7		2 S 47	12 S 6		0 N 26	23 N29		0 N 57	13 S 53
3	0 N12	0 N38	1 N 22	3 0	12 58	12 S 33	0 28	23 25	23 N 27	0 56	13 59
5	0 S 3	0 S51	0 S 7	3 14	13 49	13 24	0 30	23 20	23 22	0 56	14 5
7	0 19	2 17	1 34	3 28	14 39	14 14	0 32	23 14	23 17	0 55	14 12
9	0 35	3 42	3 0	3 42	15 27	15 3	0 34	23 8	23 11	0 55	14 18
			4 24			15 51			23 5		

11	0 51	5 5		3 56	16 14		0 36	23 2		0 55	14 25
13	1 7	6 25	5 45	4 10	17 0	16 37	0 38	22 54	22 58	0 54	14 31
15	1 23	7 42	7 4	4 24	17 44	17 22	0 40	22 47	22 51	0 54	14 38
17	1 40	8 57	8 20	4 38	18 26	18 5	0 42	22 38	22 43	0 54	14 45
19	1 55	10 8	9 33	4 52	19 6	18 46	0 44	22 30	22 34	0 53	14 52
			10 42			19 25			22 25		

21	2 11	11 16		5 6	19 44		0 46	22 20		0 53	14 59
23	2 26	12 19	11 48	5 19	20 20	20 3	0 48	22 10	22 15	0 53	15 6
25	2 40	13 18	12 49	5 33	20 55	20 38	0 50	22 0	22 5	0 52	15 13
27	2 53	14 12	13 46	5 45	21 26	21 11	0 52	21 49	21 55	0 52	15 20
29	3 4	15 1	14 37	5 58	21 56	21 41	0 54	21 38	21 44	0 52	15 27
31	3 S14	15 S 42	15 S 22	6 S 9	22 S 22	22 S 9	0 N 57	21 N27	21 N 33	0 N 52	15 S 34

FULL MOON-Sep.19, 8h. 1m. pm. (26°♓39′)

EPHEMERIS] SEPTEMBER 1994

D M	☿ Long.	♀ Long.	♂ Long.	♃ Long.	♄ Long.	♅ Long.	♆ Long.	♇ Long.	Lunar Aspects ☉	☿	♀	♂	♃	♄	♅	♆	♇
	° ′	° ′	° ′	° ′	° ′	° ′	° ′	° ′									
1	25♍42	24♎35	10♋ 6	9♏53	9♓ 2	22♑46	20♑50	25♏29				☌	△	△		☍	⚼
2	27 18	25 29	10 44	10 2	8R 57	22R 44	20R 49	25 30	∠	⚹	□			⚼	☍		△
3	28♍54	26 22	11 21	10 11	8 52	22 43	20 48	25 31	⚺	∠		⚺	□				
4	0♎28	27 15	11 59	10 21	8 48	22 42	20 47	25 32		⚺	⚹	∠					□
5	2 0	28 7	12 36	10 30	8 43	22 40	20 46	25 33	☌		∠	⚹	⚹	☍	⚼	⚼	
6	3 32	28 58	13 14	10 40	8 39	22 39	20 45	25 34			⚺		∠		△	△	⚹
7	5 2	29♎49	13 51	10 50	8 34	22 38	20 45	25 35	⚺	☌		□	⚺				∠
8	6 31	0♏39	14 28	11 0	8 30	22 37	20 44	25 36						⚼	□	□	⚺
9	7 59	1 29	15 5	11 10	8 25	22 36	20 43	25 37	∠	⚺	☌		☌	△			
10	9 26	2 18	15 42	11 20	8 21	22 35	20 42	25 38	⚹	∠		△			⚹	⚹	☌
11	10 51	3 6	16 19	11 30	8 16	22 34	20 42	25 39		⚹	⚺	⚼	⚺	□	∠	∠	
12	12 15	3 53	16 56	11 40	8 12	22 33	20 41	25 40	□		∠				⚺	⚺	⚺
13	13 38	4 39	17 33	11 50	8 7	22 32	20 40	25 42			⚹		∠	⚹			
14	14 59	5 25	18 9	12 1	8 3	22 31	20 40	25 43	△	□		☍	⚹	∠	☌	☌	∠
15	16 19	6 10	18 46	12 11	7 59	22 30	20 39	25 44			□						⚹
16	17 38	6 53	19 22	12 22	7 54	22 29	20 39	25 46	⚼	△			□	⚺			
17	18 55	7 36	19 58	12 33	7 50	22 29	20 38	25 47							⚺	⚺	□
18	20 11	8 18	20 34	12 43	7 46	22 28	20 38	25 48		⚼	△	⚼	△	☌	∠	∠	
19	21 25	8 59	21 10	12 54	7 41	22 27	20 37	25 50	☍		⚼	△	⚼		⚹	⚹	△
20	22 37	9 39	21 46	13 5	7 37	22 27	20 37	25 51						⚺			⚼
21	23 48	10 17	22 22	13 16	7 33	22 26	20 36	25 53				□		∠	□	□	
22	24 56	10 55	22 57	13 27	7 29	22 26	20 36	25 54		☍							
23	26 3	11 31	23 33	13 38	7 25	22 25	20 36	25 56	⚼		☍		☍	⚹			
24	27 8	12 6	24 8	13 50	7 21	22 25	20 36	25 57				⚹			△	△	☍
25	28 10	12 40	24 43	14 1	7 17	22 24	20 35	25 59	△			∠		□	⚼	⚼	
26	29♎10	13 12	25 19	14 12	7 13	22 24	20 35	26 1		⚼							
27	0♏ 7	13 43	25 53	14 24	7 9	22 24	20 35	26 2		△	⚼	⚺	⚼				
28	1 2	14 12	26 28	14 35	7 6	22 24	20 35	26 4	□		△		△	△			⚼
29	1 53	14 40	27 3	14 47	7 2	22 23	20 35	26 6				☌		⚼	☍	☍	△
30	2♏41	15♏ 7	27♋38	14♏58	6♓58	22♑23	20♑35	26♏ 7	⚹	□							

D M	Saturn Lat.	Saturn Dec.	Uranus Lat.	Uranus Dec.	Neptune Lat.	Neptune Dec.	Pluto Lat.	Pluto Dec.
	° ′	° ′	° ′	° ′	° ′	° ′	° ′	° ′
1	1S59	10S 1	0S31	22S 2	0N36	21S14	13N42	5S48
3	1 59	10 5	0 31	22 2	0 36	21 14	13 41	5 49
5	1 59	10 8	0 31	22 3	0 36	21 14	13 40	5 51
7	1 59	10 12	0 31	22 3	0 36	21 15	13 39	5 52
9	1 59	10 15	0 31	22 4	0 36	21 15	13 38	5 54
11	1 59	10 18	0 31	22 4	0 36	21 15	13 37	5 55
13	1 59	10 22	0 31	22 4	0 36	21 15	13 36	5 57
15	1 59	10 25	0 31	22 4	0 36	21 16	13 35	5 58
17	1 59	10 28	0 31	22 5	0 36	21 16	13 34	6 0
19	1 59	10 32	0 31	22 5	0 36	21 16	13 33	6 1
21	1 59	10 35	0 31	22 5	0 36	21 16	13 33	6 3
23	1 59	10 38	0 31	22 5	0 36	21 16	13 32	6 4
25	1 59	10 40	0 31	22 5	0 36	21 17	13 31	6 6
27	1 59	10 43	0 31	22 5	0 35	21 17	13 30	6 7
29	1 59	10 46	0 31	22 5	0 35	21 17	13 29	6 9
31	1S59	10S49	0S31	22S 5	0N35	21S17	13N28	6S10

Mutual Aspects

1 ☉☍♄. ☿⚹♇. ♂△♃.
2 ☉⚹♃. ♀⚺♇. ♂⚼♇.
5 ☉⚹♂.
6 ☉Q♇. ♃Q♅. ♀P♃.
7 ☿⊥♃. ☉P♇.
8 ☉∠♀.
9 ☿∇♄.
10 ☉P☿.
11 ☿∠♇.
12 ☿⚺♃. ☿P♇.
13 ☉△♆. ☿±♄.
15 ☉△♅.
17 ♀△♄.
18 ☉⚹♇. ☿□♆. ☿⊥♇. ♀Q♆. ♂☍♆.
19 ☿□♂.
20 ☿⚼♄. ☿□♅. ☿P♄.
21 ☉∠♃. ♀Q♅. ♂⚼♄. ♂☍♅.
23 ☿⚺♇. ♄∠♅.
24 ♂P♅.
26 ♀P♆.
27 ♂△♇.
28 ♀P♂.
29 ♀☌♃.
30 ☉∇♄. ☿P♃. ♀P♅.

LAST QUARTER-Sep.28, 0h.23m. am. (4°♋39′)

20				OCTOBER		1994			[RAPHAEL'S

D	D	Sidereal	☉	☉	☽	☽	☽	☽	Midnight	
M	W	Time	Long.	Dec.	Long.	Lat.	Dec.	Node	☽ Long.	☽ Dec.

		H. M. S.	° ′ ″	° ′	° ′ ″	° ′	° ′	° ′	° ′ ″	° ′
1	S	12 39 57	8 ♎ 4 49	3 S 12	19 ♋ 19 49	5 S 11	10 N 6	16 ♏ 37	26 ♋ 9 44	7 N59
2	Su	12 43 54	9 3 51	3 36	3 ♍ 6 21	4 57	5 45	16 33	10 ♍ 9 27	3 N23
3	M	12 47 50	10 2 56	3 59	17 18 37	4 24	0 N57	16 30	24 33 14	1 S 32
4	T	12 51 47	11 2 2	4 22	1 ♎ 52 36	3 34	4 S 1	16 27	9 ♎ 15 49	6 29
5	W	12 55 44	12 1 11	4 45	16 41 56	2 29	8 51	16 24	24 9 53	11 6
6	Th	12 59 40	13 0 21	5 8	1 ♏ 38 38	1 S 13	13 11	16 21	9 ♏ 7 6	15 3
7	F	13 3 37	13 59 34	5 31	16 34 20	0 N 8	16 39	16 18	23 59 24	17 59
8	S	13 7 33	14 58 48	5 54	1 ♐ 21 32	1 28	18 59	16 14	8 ♐ 40 4	19 40
9	Su	13 11 30	15 58 4	6 17	15 54 28	2 42	20 1	16 11	23 4 22	20 2
10	M	13 15 26	16 57 23	6 40	0 ♑ 9 29	3 43	19 43	16 8	7 ♑ 9 41	19 7
11	T	13 19 23	17 56 42	7 2	14 4 55	4 30	18 13	16 5	20 55 14	17 5
12	W	13 23 19	18 56 4	7 25	27 40 43	5 0	15 43	16 2	4 ♒ 21 32	14 10
13	Th	13 27 16	19 55 27	7 47	10 ♒ 57 53	5 14	12 27	15 58	17 29 57	10 36
14	F	13 31 13	20 54 52	8 10	23 58 0	5 11	8 38	15 55	0 ♓ 22 13	6 36
15	S	13 35 9	21 54 19	8 32	6 ♓ 42 51	4 53	4 31	15 52	13 0 8	2 S 24
16	Su	13 39 6	22 53 47	8 54	19 14 15	4 20	0 S 16	15 49	25 25 26	1 N51
17	M	13 43 2	23 53 18	9 16	1 ♈ 33 53	3 37	3 N56	15 46	7 ♈ 39 47	5 58
18	T	13 46 59	24 52 50	9 38	13 43 21	2 43	7 55	15 43	19 44 47	9 47
19	W	13 50 55	25 52 24	10 0	25 44 17	1 43	11 33	15 39	1 ♉ 42 5	13 11
20	Th	13 54 52	26 52 1	10 21	7 ♉ 38 25	0 N39	14 41	15 36	13 33 34	16 1
21	F	13 58 48	27 51 39	10 43	19 27 48	0 S 26	17 11	15 33	25 21 26	18 9
22	S	14 2 45	28 51 20	11 4	1 ♊ 14 50	1 30	18 56	15 30	7 ♊ 8 20	19 31
23	Su	14 6 42	29 ♎ 51 2	11 25	13 2 23	2 31	19 52	15 27	18 57 24	20 1
24	M	14 10 38	0 ♏ 50 47	11 46	24 53 52	3 25	19 56	15 24	0 ♋ 52 16	19 37
25	T	14 14 35	1 50 34	12 7	6 ♋ 53 8	4 11	19 5	15 20	12 56 59	18 20
26	W	14 18 31	2 50 23	12 27	19 4 24	4 46	17 21	15 17	25 15 56	16 10
27	Th	14 22 28	3 50 15	12 48	1 ♌ 32 8	5 9	14 45	15 14	7 ♌ 53 30	13 13
28	F	14 26 24	4 50 9	13 8	14 20 33	5 18	11 27	15 11	20 53 43	9 32
29	S	14 30 21	5 50 4	13 28	27 33 21	5 10	7 28	15 8	4 ♍ 19 44	5 16
30	Su	14 34 17	6 50 2	13 48	11 ♍ 13 0	4 45	2 N58	15 4	18 13 11	0 N35
31	M	14 38 14	7 ♏ 50 1	14 S 7	25 ♍ 20 7	4 S 2	1 S 51	15 ♏ 1	2 ♎ 33 30	4 S 17

D	Mercury			Venus			Mars			Jupiter	
M	Lat.	Dec.		Lat.	Dec.		Lat.	Dec.		Lat.	Dec.
1	3 S 14	15 S 42	16 S 0	6 S 9	22 S 22	22 S 34	0 N 57	21 N27	21 N 21	0 N 52	15 S 34
3	3 22	16 16	16 30	6 20	22 46	22 57	0 59	21 15	21 9	0 51	15 41
5	3 28	16 41	16 49	6 30	23 7	23 16	1 1	21 3	21 9	0 51	15 48
7	3 30	16 55	16 58	6 39	23 24	23 31	1 4	20 50	20 56	0 51	15 55
9	3 28	16 57	16 52	6 47	23 38	23 43	1 6	20 37	20 44	0 51	16 2
11	3 21	16 44	16 31	6 54	23 47	23 51	1 8	20 24	20 31	0 50	16 9
13	3 8	16 15	15 53	6 59	23 53	23 54	1 11	20 11	20 18	0 50	16 17
15	2 48	15 27	14 57	7 2	23 54	23 53	1 13	19 57	20 4	0 50	16 24
17	2 20	14 22	13 44	7 3	23 51	23 47	1 16	19 44	19 51	0 50	16 31
19	1 46	13 2	12 18	7 1	23 42	23 35	1 18	19 30	19 37	0 49	16 38
21	1 7	11 32	10 46	6 57	23 28	23 18	1 21	19 16	19 23	0 49	16 45
23	0 S 26	10 2	9 19	6 50	23 8	22 56	1 23	19 2	19 9	0 49	16 52
25	0 N14	8 40	8 6	6 40	22 43	22 28	1 26	18 47	18 55	0 49	16 59
27	0 50	7 36	7 12	6 27	22 12	21 55	1 28	18 33	18 40	0 49	17 6
29	1 20	6 54	6 S 42	6 11	21 36	21 S 17	1 31	18 19	18 26	0 48	17 13
31	1 N43	6 S 35		5 S 51	20 S 56		1 N 34	18 N 5	18 N 12	0 N 48	17 S 20

FULL MOON-Oct.19, 0h.18m. pm. (25°♈53′)

D M	☿ Long.	♀ Long.	♂ Long.	♃ Long.	♄ Long.	♅ Long.	♆ Long.	♇ Long.	☉	☿	♀	♂	♃	♄	♅	♆	♇
	° ′	° ′	° ′	° ′	° ′	° ′	° ′	° ′									
1	3♏26	15♏32	28♋12	15♏10	6♓55	22♑23	20♑34	26♏ 9	∠		□		□				
2	4 7	15 55	28 46	15 22	6R 51	22D 23	20R 34	26 11	⊻	✱		⊻		☍	⚻	⚻	□
3	4 43	16 16	29 21	15 34	6 48	22 23	20D 34	26 13		∠	✱	∠	✱		△	△	
4	5 15	16 36	29♋55	15 46	6 44	22 23	20 34	26 15		⊻	∠	✱	∠				✱
5	5 41	16 54	0♌28	15 58	6 41	22 24	20 35	26 16	☌		⊻		⊻	⚻	□	□	∠
6	6 3	17 9	1 2	16 10	6 38	22 24	20 35	26 18		☌		□		△			⊻
7	6 18	17 23	1 36	16 22	6 35	22 24	20 35	26 20	⊻		☌		☌		✱	✱	
8	6 27	17 35	2 9	16 34	6 31	22 24	20 35	26 22	∠	⊻		△		□	∠	∠	☌
9	6R 29	17 44	2 42	16 46	6 28	22 25	20 35	26 24	✱	∠	⊻	⚻	⊻		⊻	⊻	
10	6 23	17 52	3 16	16 58	6 26	22 25	20 35	26 26		✱	∠		∠	✱			⊻
11	6 10	17 57	3 49	17 11	6 23	22 26	20 36	26 28	□		✱		✱			☌	∠
12	5 49	18 0	4 21	17 23	6 20	22 26	20 36	26 30						∠	☌		✱
13	5 20	18R 1	4 54	17 35	6 17	22 27	20 36	26 32		□		☍		⊻			
14	4 42	17 59	5 26	17 48	6 15	22 27	20 37	26 34	△		□		□		⊻	⊻	□
15	3 56	17 55	5 59	18 0	6 12	22 28	20 37	26 36	⚻	△				☌	∠	∠	
16	3 2	17 48	6 31	18 13	6 10	22 29	20 38	26 38		⚻	△	⚻	△		✱	✱	
17	2 1	17 39	7 3	18 25	6 7	22 29	20 38	26 40			⚻	△	⚻	⊻			△
18	0♏54	17 27	7 34	18 38	6 5	22 30	20 39	26 42									⚻
19	29♎43	17 13	8 6	18 51	6 3	22 31	20 39	26 44	☍	☍				∠	□	□	
20	28 29	16 57	8 37	19 3	6 1	22 32	20 40	26 46				□		✱			
21	27 14	16 38	9 9	19 16	5 59	22 33	20 40	26 49			☍		☍		△	△	
22	26 1	16 18	9 40	19 29	5 57	22 34	20 41	26 51						□		⚻	☍
23	24 52	15 54	10 11	19 42	5 55	22 35	20 42	26 53	⚻	⚻		✱			⚻		
24	23 48	15 29	10 41	19 54	5 54	22 36	20 42	26 55		△	⚻	∠					
25	22 52	15 2	11 12	20 7	5 52	22 37	20 43	26 57	△			⊻	⚻	△			⚻
26	22 6	14 33	11 42	20 20	5 51	22 39	20 44	27 0		□	△		△	⚻	☍	☍	
27	21 30	14 3	12 12	20 33	5 49	22 40	20 45	27 2	□								△
28	21 5	13 31	12 42	20 46	5 48	22 41	20 46	27 4			□	☌	□				
29	20 51	12 57	13 11	20 59	5 47	22 42	20 46	27 6		✱							□
30	20D 50	12 23	13 41	21 12	5 46	22 44	20 47	27 9	✱	∠	✱	⊻		☍	⚻	⚻	
31	20♎59	11♏47	14♌10	21♏25	5♓45	22♑45	20♑48	27♏11	∠	⊻	∠	∠	✱		△	△	✱

D M	Saturn Lat.	Saturn Dec.	Uranus Lat.	Uranus Dec.	Neptune Lat.	Neptune Dec.	Pluto Lat.	Pluto Dec.
	° ′	° ′	° ′	° ′	° ′	° ′	° ′	° ′
1	1S59	10S49	0S31	22S 5	0N35	21S17	13N28	6S10
3	1 59	10 51	0 31	22 5	0 35	21 17	13 28	6 12
5	1 58	10 53	0 31	22 5	0 35	21 17	13 27	6 13
7	1 58	10 56	0 31	22 5	0 35	21 17	13 26	6 15
9	1 58	10 58	0 31	22 5	0 35	21 17	13 25	6 16
11	1 58	11 0	0 31	22 5	0 35	21 17	13 25	6 18
13	1 58	11 2	0 31	22 4	0 35	21 17	13 24	6 20
15	1 58	11 3	0 31	22 4	0 35	21 17	13 23	6 21
17	1 57	11 5	0 31	22 4	0 35	21 17	13 23	6 23
19	1 57	11 6	0 31	22 4	0 35	21 17	13 22	6 24
21	1 57	11 8	0 31	22 3	0 35	21 17	13 21	6 26
23	1 57	11 9	0 31	22 3	0 35	21 16	13 21	6 27
25	1 56	11 10	0 30	22 2	0 35	21 16	13 20	6 28
27	1 56	11 11	0 30	22 2	0 35	21 16	13 20	6 30
29	1 56	11 11	0 30	22 2	0 35	21 16	13 19	6 31
31	1S56	11S12	0S30	22S 1	0N34	21S16	13N19	6S33

Mutual Aspects

2 ☉⊥♃. ♅Stat. ♆Stat.
3 ☉⊥♀. ♂ P ♆.
4 ☉∠♇.
5 ♂±♄.
6 ☉Q♂. ☉±♄.
9 ☿△♄. ☉P♇. ☿Stat.
10 ☉⊻♃. ☿△♄.
11 ☉⊻♀.
13 ☿□♂. ☿ P ♃. ♀Stat.
14 ☉⚻♄. ☉□♆. ☉⊥♇.
15 ♀☌♃. ♂▽♄.
16 ☉□♅.
20 ☉⊻♇.
21 ☉⊻☿. ☿⊻♇.
22 ☉P☿. ☉P♄. ☿P♄.
25 ☿Q♂. ☿□♅.
28 ☿⊥♇. ♃✱♆. ♀P♅.
29 ☉△♄. ☿⊻♃. ♀□♂. ♄∠♆.
30 ♀P♆. ☿Stat.

LAST QUARTER-Oct.27, 4h.44m. pm. (4°♌ 2′)

22					NOVEMBER		1994			[RAPHAEL'S
D M	D W	Sidereal Time	☉ Long.	☉ Dec.	☽ Long.	☽ Lat.	☽ Dec.	Node	Midnight ☽ Long.	☽ Dec.
		H. M. S.								
1	T	14 42 11	8♏50 5	14 S 27	9♎52 50	3 S 2	6 S 42	14♏58	17♎17 27	9 S 3
2	W	14 46 7	9 50 9	14 46	24 46 29	1 49	11 17	14 55	2♏18 58	13 21
3	Th	14 50 4	10 50 15	15 5	9♏53 48	0 S 27	15 13	14 52	17 29 46	16 49
4	F	14 54 0	11 50 24	15 23	25 5 40	0 N 57	18 7	14 49	2♐40 17	19 6
5	S	14 57 57	12 50 34	15 42	10♐12 29	2 17	19 43	14 45	17 41 13	20 0
6	Su	15 1 53	13 50 45	16 0	25 5 35	3 26	19 55	14 42	2♑24 48	19 30
7	M	15 5 50	14 50 59	16 17	9♑38 18	4 20	18 46	14 39	16 45 39	17 44
8	T	15 9 46	15 51 14	16 35	23 46 38	4 57	16 28	14 36	0♒41 8	14 59
9	W	15 13 43	16 51 30	16 52	7♒29 13	5 16	13 18	14 33	14 11 1	11 29
10	Th	15 17 40	17 51 47	17 9	20 46 48	5 16	9 34	14 30	27 16 55	7 33
11	F	15 21 36	18 52 6	17 26	3♓41 44	5 1	5 28	14 26	10♓ 1 41	3 S 22
12	S	15 25 33	19 52 27	17 42	16 17 12	4 32	1 S 14	14 23	22 28 44	0 N 53
13	Su	15 29 29	20 52 49	17 58	28 36 46	3 50	2 N 58	14 20	4♈41 43	5 0
14	M	15 33 26	21 53 12	18 14	10♈44 2	2 59	6 59	14 17	16 44 5	8 53
15	T	15 37 22	22 53 37	18 30	22 42 18	2 0	10 41	14 14	28 39 0	12 23
16	W	15 41 19	23 54 3	18 45	4♉34 33	0 N 57	13 56	14 10	10♉29 15	15 21
17	Th	15 45 15	24 54 31	19 0	16 23 25	0 S 9	16 36	14 7	22 17 41	17 41
18	F	15 49 12	25 55 0	19 14	28 11 12	1 13	18 34	14 4	4♊ 5 22	19 15
19	S	15 53 9	26 55 31	19 28	10♊ 0 3	2 15	19 43	14 1	15 55 32	19 59
20	Su	15 57 5	27 56 3	19 42	21 52 4	3 11	20 0	13 58	27 49 56	19 49
21	M	16 1 2	28 56 38	19 55	3♋49 25	3 59	19 24	13 55	9♋50 51	18 45
22	T	16 4 58	29♏57 13	20 8	15 54 32	4 37	17 54	13 51	22 0 51	16 50
23	W	16 8 55	0♐57 51	20 21	28 10 8	5 3	15 34	13 48	4♌22 48	14 7
24	Th	16 12 51	1 58 30	20 33	10♌39 14	5 16	12 30	13 45	16 59 52	10 43
25	F	16 16 48	2 59 10	20 45	23 25 5	5 13	8 47	13 42	29 55 18	6 44
26	S	16 20 44	3 59 52	20 57	6♍30 53	4 54	4 N 34	13 39	13♍12 10	2 N 19
27	Su	16 24 41	5 0 36	21 8	19 59 27	4 18	0 0	13 36	26 52 56	2 S 21
28	M	16 28 38	6 1 22	21 19	3♎52 41	3 27	4 S 42	13 32	10♎58 43	7 2
29	T	16 32 34	7 2 9	21 29	18 10 52	2 21	9 18	13 29	25 28 49	11 28
30	W	16 36 31	8♐ 2 57	21 S 39	2♏52 3	1 S 5	13 S 29	13♏26	10♏19 54	15 S 18

D M	Mercury Lat.	Mercury Dec.	Mercury Dec.	Venus Lat.	Venus Dec.	Venus Dec.	Mars Lat.	Mars Dec.	Mars Dec.	Jupiter Lat.	Jupiter Dec.
1	1 N52	6 S 34	6 S 39	5 S 41	20 S 34	20 S 12	1 N 35	17 N 57	17 N 50	0 N 48	17 S 24
3	2 5	6 48	7 1	5 17	19 49	19 25	1 38	17 43	17 36	0 48	17 31
5	2 12	7 18	7 39	4 51	19 1	18 36	1 41	17 29	17 22	0 48	17 38
7	2 14	8 2	8 28	4 23	18 11	17 46	1 44	17 15	17 8	0 48	17 44
9	2 12	8 56	9 26	3 54	17 22	16 57	1 47	17 1	16 54	0 48	17 51
11	2 7	9 57	10 29	3 23	16 33	16 9	1 50	16 47	16 41	0 47	17 58
13	1 59	11 2	11 35	2 53	15 46	15 24	1 53	16 34	16 27	0 47	18 5
15	1 50	12 9	12 44	2 22	15 2	14 41	1 56	16 21	16 14	0 47	18 11
17	1 38	13 18	13 52	1 52	14 21	14 2	1 59	16 8	16 1	0 47	18 18
19	1 26	14 26	15 0	1 22	13 45	13 28	2 3	15 55	15 49	0 47	18 24
21	1 13	15 33	16 6	0 54	13 13	12 58	2 6	15 43	15 37	0 47	18 31
23	1 0	16 38	17 10	0 27	12 45	12 33	2 9	15 31	15 25	0 47	18 37
25	0 46	17 41	18 11	0 S 1	12 22	12 13	2 13	15 19	15 13	0 47	18 43
27	0 32	18 41	19 10	0 N 23	12 4	11 57	2 16	15 8	15 2	0 46	18 49
29	0 18	19 37	20 S 4	0 46	11 51	11 S 46	2 20	14 57	14 N 52	0 46	18 55
31	0 N 4	20 S 30		1 N 7	11 S 42		2 N 24	14 N 47		0 N 46	19 S 1

FULL MOON-Nov.18, 6h.57m. am. (25°♉42′)

D M	☿ Long.	♀ Long.	♂ Long.	♃ Long.	♄ Long.	♅ Long.	♆ Long.	♇ Long.	Lunar Aspects ☉	☿	♀	♂	♃	♄	♅	♆	♇
	° ′	° ′	° ′	° ′	° ′	° ′	° ′	° ′									
1	21♎18	11♏12	14♌39	21♏38	5♓44	22♑47	20♑49	27♏13	⚺		⚺	⚹	∠				∠
2	21 48	10R 35	15 8	21 51	5R 43	22 48	20 50	27 15		☌			⚺	⚼	□	□	⚺
3	22 27	9 59	15 36	22 5	5 43	22 50	20 51	27 18	●		☌	□		△			
4	23 13	9 22	16 4	22 18	5 42	22 52	20 52	27 20		⚺			●		⚹	⚹	☌
5	24 7	8 46	16 32	22 31	5 42	22 53	20 53	27 22	⚺	∠	⚺	△		□	∠	∠	
6	25 7	8 11	17 0	22 44	5 41	22 55	20 55	27 25	∠	⚹	∠	⚼	⚺		⚺	⚺	⚺
7	26 13	7 36	17 28	22 57	5 41	22 57	20 56	27 27	⚹		⚹		∠	⚹			∠
8	27 24	7 3	17 55	23 10	5 41	22 59	20 57	27 29		□			⚹	∠	☌	☌	⚹
9	28 39	6 30	18 22	23 24	5D 41	23 1	20 58	27 32			□			⚺			
10	29♎57	5 59	18 48	23 37	5 41	23 2	20 59	27 34	□			☍	□		⚺	⚺	
11	1♏19	5 30	19 15	23 50	5 41	23 4	21 1	27 37		△	△			☌	∠	∠	□
12	2 43	5 2	19 41	24 3	5 41	23 6	21 2	27 39	△	⚼	⚼					⚹	
13	4 9	4 37	20 7	24 17	5 42	23 8	21 3	27 41					△		⚹		△
14	5 37	4 13	20 32	24 30	5 42	23 11	21 5	27 44	⚼			⚼	⚼	⚺			⚼
15	7 6	3 52	20 58	24 43	5 43	23 13	21 6	27 46				△		∠	□	□	
16	8 37	3 33	21 22	24 57	5 43	23 15	21 7	27 49		☍	☍			⚹			
17	10 8	3 17	21 47	25 10	5 44	23 17	21 9	27 51				□				△	
18	11 40	3 2	22 11	25 23	5 45	23 19	21 10	27 53	☍				☍		△		☍
19	13 13	2 51	22 35	25 36	5 46	23 22	21 12	27 56						□	⚼	⚼	
20	14 46	2 42	22 59	25 50	5 47	23 24	21 13	27 58			⚼	⚹					
21	16 20	2 35	23 22	26 3	5 48	23 26	21 15	28 1		⚼	△	∠		△			
22	17 54	2 31	23 45	26 16	5 50	23 29	21 16	28 3	⚼	△			⚼	⚼		☍	⚼
23	19 28	2 29	24 8	26 30	5 51	23 31	21 18	28 5	△		□	⚺	△		☍		△
24	21 3	2D 30	24 30	26 43	5 53	23 34	21 20	28 8									
25	22 37	2 33	24 52	26 56	5 54	23 36	21 21	28 10		□		☌	□				□
26	24 11	2 38	25 14	27 9	5 56	23 39	21 23	28 12	□		⚹			☍	⚼	⚼	
27	25 46	2 46	25 35	27 23	5 58	23 41	21 25	28 15		⚹	∠	⚺			△	△	
28	27 20	2 56	25 56	27 36	6 0	23 44	21 26	28 17	⚹		⚺		⚹				⚹
29	28 55	3 9	26 16	27 49	6 2	23 47	21 28	28 20	∠	∠		∠	∠	⚼	□	□	∠
30	0♐29	3♏23	26♌36	28♏2	6♓4	23♑49	21♑30	28♏22	⚺	⚺	☌	⚹	⚺	△			⚺

D M	Saturn Lat.	Saturn Dec.	Uranus Lat.	Uranus Dec.	Neptune Lat.	Neptune Dec.	Pluto Lat.	Pluto Dec.
	° ′	° ′	° ′	° ′	° ′	° ′	° ′	° ′
1	1S56	11S12	0S30	22S 1	0N34	21S15	13N19	6S33
3	1 55	11 12	0 30	22 0	0 34	21 15	13 18	6 35
5	1 55	11 12	0 30	22 0	0 34	21 15	13 18	6 36
7	1 55	11 12	0 30	21 59	0 34	21 15	13 18	6 37
9	1 55	11 12	0 30	21 58	0 34	21 14	13 17	6 39
11	1 54	11 12	0 30	21 58	0 34	21 14	13 17	6 40
13	1 54	11 11	0 30	21 57	0 34	21 14	13 17	6 41
15	1 54	11 11	0 30	21 56	0 34	21 13	13 17	6 42
17	1 53	11 10	0 30	21 55	0 34	21 13	13 16	6 44
19	1 53	11 9	0 30	21 55	0 34	21 13	13 16	6 45
21	1 53	11 8	0 30	21 54	0 34	21 12	13 16	6 46
23	1 53	11 6	0 30	21 53	0 34	21 12	13 16	6 47
25	1 52	11 5	0 30	21 52	0 34	21 11	13 16	6 48
27	1 52	11 3	0 30	21 51	0 34	21 11	13 16	6 49
29	1 52	11 2	0 30	21 50	0 34	21 10	13 16	6 50
31	1S51	11S 0	0S30	21S49	0N34	21S10	13N16	6S51

1 ☉Q♆. ☿⊥♇.
2 ☉⊥♀. ☿⚺♃. ♀Q♅.
3 ☉Q♅.
4 ☿□♅. ♂P♃.
5 ♀Q♆.
7 ♃⚹♅.
8 ☿⚺♇. ♀P♃.
9 ☉P♂. ♄Stat.
10 ☉P♀. ♀P♂.
11 ☿Q♂. ♀△♄.
12 ☉□♂.
13 ☉⚹♆. ☿☌♀. ☉P♃. ☿P♄.
14 ☿△♄.
15 ☉⚹♅. ♂▽♆.
16 ☿Q♆. ♀Q♂.
17 ☉☌♃.
18 ☿Q♅. ☿P♀.
20 ☉☌♇.
21 ♂▽♅. ☿P♂.
23 ♀Stat.
24 ☿⚹♆.
25 ☉⚺♀.
26 ☿⚹♅.
27 ☿□♂. ☉P♆. ☿P♃.
28 ☉□♄. ☉∠♆. ☿☌♃.
29 ☿☌♇.

LAST QUARTER-Nov.26, 7h. 4m. am. (3°♍47′)

| 24 | | | | | DECEMBER | 1994 | | | [RAPHAEL'S | |

D M	D W	Sidereal Time	☉ Long.	☉ Dec.	☽ Long.	☽ Lat.	☽ Dec.	Node	Midnight ☽ Long.	☽ Dec.
		H. M. S.	° ′ ″	° ′	° ′ ″	° ′	° ′	° ′	° ′ ″	° ′
1	Th	16 40 27	9 ♐ 3 47	21 S 48	17 ♏ 51 33	0 N17	16 S 53	13 ♏ 23	25 ♏ 59 59	18 S 10
2	F	16 44 24	10 4 39	21 58	3 ♐ 2 4	1 39	19 8	13 20	10 ♐ 38 35	19 46
3	S	16 48 20	11 5 31	22 6	18 14 16	2 54	20 2	13 16	25 47 51	19 56
4	Su	16 52 17	12 6 25	22 14	3 ♑ 18 9	3 56	19 28	13 13	10 ♑ 44 3	18 40
5	M	16 56 13	13 7 20	22 22	18 4 37	4 41	17 34	13 10	25 19 6	16 13
6	T	17 0 10	14 8 15	22 30	2 ≈ 26 54	5 7	14 38	13 7	9 ≈ 27 39	12 52
7	W	17 4 7	15 9 11	22 37	16 21 11	5 13	10 57	13 4	23 7 29	8 55
8	Th	17 8 3	16 10 8	22 43	29 46 43	5 2	6 49	13 1	6 ♓ 19 11	4 41
9	F	17 12 0	17 11 6	22 49	12 ♓ 45 15	4 36	2 S 31	12 57	19 5 27	0 S 22
10	S	17 15 56	18 12 4	22 55	25 20 17	3 57	1 N46	12 53	1 ♈ 30 23	3 N52
11	Su	17 19 53	19 13 2	23 0	7 ♈ 36 19	3 8	5 54	12 51	13 38 43	7 51
12	M	17 23 49	20 14 2	23 5	19 38 13	2 11	9 43	12 48	25 35 23	11 28
13	T	17 27 46	21 15 2	23 9	1 ♉ 30 48	1 10	13 6	12 45	7 ♉ 25 0	14 35
14	W	17 31 42	22 16 2	23 13	13 18 29	0 N 6	15 56	12 41	19 11 44	17 6
15	Th	17 35 39	23 17 4	23 16	25 5 10	0 S 58	18 6	12 38	0 ♊ 59 9	18 54
16	F	17 39 36	24 18 5	23 19	6 ♊ 54 2	1 59	19 30	12 35	12 50 7	19 53
17	S	17 43 32	25 19 8	23 21	18 47 39	2 56	20 3	12 32	24 46 52	19 59
18	Su	17 47 29	26 20 11	23 23	0 ♋ 47 57	3 45	19 41	12 29	6 ♋ 51 4	19 10
19	M	17 51 25	27 21 15	23 25	12 56 23	4 24	18 25	12 26	19 4 0	17 28
20	T	17 55 22	28 22 19	23 26	25 14 5	4 52	16 18	12 22	1 ♌ 26 44	14 56
21	W	17 59 18	29 ♐ 23 24	23 26	7 ♌ 42 7	5 6	13 24	12 19	14 0 21	11 42
22	Th	18 3 15	0 ♑ 24 29	23 26	20 21 37	5 6	9 51	12 16	26 46 7	7 53
23	F	18 7 11	1 25 36	23 26	3 ♍ 14 2	4 50	5 48	12 13	9 ♍ 45 35	3 N38
24	S	18 11 8	2 26 43	23 25	16 21 2	4 19	1 N24	12 10	23 0 36	0 S 52
25	Su	18 15 5	3 27 50	23 24	29 44 32	3 34	3 S 10	12 7	6 ♎ 33 4	5 27
26	M	18 19 1	4 28 58	23 22	13 ♎ 26 21	2 35	7 41	12 3	20 24 33	9 51
27	T	18 22 58	5 30 7	23 19	27 27 42	1 25	11 54	12 0	4 ♏ 35 46	13 48
28	W	18 26 54	6 31 17	23 17	11 ♏ 48 34	0 S 9	15 31	11 57	19 5 48	17 1
29	Th	18 30 51	7 32 27	23 13	26 27 1	1 N 9	18 14	11 54	3 ♐ 51 35	19 10
30	F	18 34 47	8 33 37	23 10	11 ♐ 18 44	2 24	19 46	11 51	18 47 33	20 1
31	S	18 38 44	9 ♑ 34 48	23 S 6	26 ♐ 16 58	3 N29	19 S 55	11 ♏ 47	3 ♑ 45 53	19 S 27

D M	Mercury		Venus		Mars		Jupiter	
	Lat.	Dec.	Lat.	Dec.	Lat.	Dec.	Lat.	Dec.
	° ′	° ′	° ′	° ′	° ′	° ′	° ′	° ′
1	0 N 4	20 S 30	1 N 7	11 S 42	2 N 24	14 N47	0 N 46	19 S 1
3	0 S 10	21 19	1 26	11 37	2 27	14 38	0 46	19 7
5	0 23	22 4	1 44	11 35	2 31	14 29	0 46	19 13
7	0 36	22 45	2 0	11 38	2 35	14 20	0 46	19 19
9	0 48	23 21	2 15	11 44	2 39	14 13	0 46	19 24
11	1 0	23 53	2 28	11 52	2 43	14 6	0 46	19 30
13	1 12	24 19	2 40	12 4	2 47	14 0	0 46	19 35
15	1 22	24 40	2 51	12 18	2 51	13 54	0 46	19 40
17	1 32	24 56	3 0	12 34	2 56	13 50	0 46	19 46
19	1 41	25 7	3 8	12 52	3 0	13 46	0 46	19 51
21	1 49	25 12	3 16	13 12	3 4	13 43	0 46	19 56
23	1 56	25 11	3 22	13 33	3 9	13 42	0 46	20 1
25	2 1	25 5	3 27	13 56	3 13	13 41	0 46	20 5
27	2 6	24 52	3 31	14 19	3 18	13 41	0 46	20 10
29	2 8	24 34	3 34	14 43	3 22	13 42	0 46	20 15
31	2 S 10	24 S 9	3 N 36	15 S 8	3 N 27	13 N43	0 N 46	20 S 19

FULL MOON-Dec.18, 2h.17m. am. (25° ♊ 55′)

D M	☿ Long.	♀ Long.	♂ Long.	♃ Long.	♄ Long.	♅ Long.	♆ Long.	♇ Long.	Lunar Aspects ☉	☿	♀	♂	♃	♄	♅	♆	♇
	° ′	° ′	° ′	° ′	° ′	° ′	° ′	° ′									
1	2 ♐ 3	3 ♏ 40	26 ♌ 56	28 ♏ 16	6 ♓ 6	23 ♑ 52	21 ♑ 32	28 ♏ 24							⚹	⚹	
2	3 38	3 58	27 15	28 29	6 9	23 55	21 33	28 27	☌	☌	⚺	□	●	□	∠	∠	☌
3	5 12	4 19	27 34	28 42	6 11	23 58	21 35	28 29			∠				⚺	⚺	
4	6 46	4 41	27 52	28 55	6 14	24 1	21 37	28 31		⚺	⚹	△	⚺	⚹			⚺
5	8 20	5 6	28 10	29 8	6 16	24 3	21 39	28 34	⚺	∠		⚻	∠	∠	☌	☌	∠
6	9 54	5 32	28 27	29 21	6 19	24 6	21 41	28 36	∠		□		⚹	⚺			⚹
7	11 29	6 0	28 44	29 34	6 22	24 9	21 43	28 38	⚹	⚹						⚺	
8	13 3	6 29	29 0	29 ♏ 48	6 25	24 12	21 45	28 41				☍	□		⚺		□
9	14 37	7 0	29 16	0 ♐ 1	6 28	24 15	21 47	28 43	□	□	△			☌	∠	∠	
10	16 11	7 32	29 31	0 14	6 31	24 18	21 49	28 45			⚻		△		⚹	⚹	△
11	17 45	8 6	29 ♌ 46	0 27	6 34	24 21	21 50	28 48						⚺			
12	19 19	8 42	0 ♍ 0	0 40	6 38	24 24	21 52	28 50	△	△		⚻	⚻	∠	□	□	⚻
13	20 54	9 19	0 14	0 52	6 41	24 27	21 54	28 52	⚻	⚻		△		⚹			
14	22 28	9 57	0 27	1 5	6 44	24 30	21 57	28 54			☍						
15	24 3	10 36	0 40	1 18	6 48	24 34	21 59	28 57				□			△	△	☍
16	25 37	11 17	0 52	1 31	6 52	24 37	22 1	28 59					☍	□	⚻	⚻	
17	27 12	11 58	1 4	1 44	6 55	24 40	22 3	29 1									
18	28 ♐ 47	12 41	1 15	1 56	6 59	24 43	22 5	29 3	☍	☍	⚻	⚹					
19	0 ♑ 22	13 25	1 25	2 9	7 3	24 46	22 7	29 6			△	∠	⚻	△			⚻
20	1 57	14 10	1 35	2 22	7 7	24 50	22 9	29 8						⚻	☍	☍	△
21	3 33	14 56	1 44	2 34	7 11	24 53	22 11	29 10				⚺	△				
22	5 8	15 43	1 52	2 47	7 16	24 56	22 13	29 12	⚻	⚻	□						
23	6 44	16 31	2 0	3 0	7 20	25 0	22 15	29 14	△	△		☌	□	☍		⚻	□
24	8 20	17 20	2 7	3 12	7 24	25 3	22 18	29 16			⚹				⚻	△	
25	9 56	18 10	2 14	3 24	7 29	25 6	22 20	29 18	□		∠	⚺	⚹		△		⚹
26	11 33	19 0	2 20	3 37	7 33	25 10	22 22	29 20		□	⚺	∠	∠				∠
27	13 9	19 52	2 25	3 49	7 38	25 13	22 24	29 22				⚹	⚺	⚻	□	□	⚺
28	14 46	20 44	2 29	4 1	7 42	25 16	22 26	29 24	⚹	⚹				△			
29	16 23	21 36	2 33	4 14	7 47	25 20	22 29	29 26	∠	∠	☌	□			⚹	⚹	☌
30	18 0	22 30	2 36	4 26	7 52	25 23	22 31	29 28	⚺				●	□	∠	∠	
31	19 ♑ 37	23 ♏ 24	2 ♍ 38	4 ♐ 38	7 ♓ 57	25 ♑ 27	22 ♑ 33	29 ♏ 30		⚺	⚺	△			⚺	⚺	⚺

D M	Saturn Lat.	Saturn Dec.	Uranus Lat.	Uranus Dec.	Neptune Lat.	Neptune Dec.	Pluto Lat.	Pluto Dec.
	° ′	° ′	° ′	° ′	° ′	° ′	° ′	° ′
1	1S51	11S 0	0S30	21S49	0N34	21S10	13N16	6S51
3	1 51	10 58	0 30	21 48	0 34	21 9	13 16	6 52
5	1 51	10 56	0 30	21 47	0 34	21 9	13 16	6 53
7	1 51	10 53	0 30	21 46	0 34	21 8	13 16	6 54
9	1 50	10 51	0 30	21 45	0 34	21 8	13 16	6 54
11	1 50	10 48	0 30	21 44	0 33	21 7	13 16	6 55
13	1 50	10 46	0 30	21 43	0 33	21 6	13 17	6 56
15	1 50	10 43	0 30	21 42	0 33	21 6	13 17	6 57
17	1 49	10 40	0 30	21 41	0 33	21 5	13 17	6 57
19	1 49	10 37	0 30	21 40	0 33	21 4	13 17	6 58
21	1 49	10 33	0 30	21 38	0 33	21 4	13 18	6 58
23	1 49	10 30	0 30	21 37	0 33	21 3	13 18	6 59
25	1 48	10 26	0 30	21 36	0 33	21 3	13 18	6 59
27	1 48	10 23	0 30	21 35	0 33	21 2	13 19	7 0
29	1 48	10 19	0 30	21 33	0 33	21 1	13 19	7 0
31	1S48	10S15	0S30	21S32	0N33	21S 0	13N19	7S 1

1 ☉∠♅. ☉P♅.
2 ☉⊥♀. ☿⚺♀. ♃☌♇.
3 ♂±♆. ☿P♆.
4 ☿□♄. ☿∠♆. ☿P♅.
5 ☿∠♅.
6 ☉P☿.
7 ☿⊥♀. ♂□♇.
8 ☉⊥♆. ♀△♄.
10 ☉⊥♅. ☿⊥♆.
11 ☿⊥♅.
14 ☉☌☿. ☉⚺♆. ☿⚺♆. ♀Q♆. ♂±♅.
15 ☿Q♄. ☿⚺♅.
16 ☉⚺♅.
17 ☉Q♄. ☿∠♀.
18 ☿⚺♇. ♀Q♅.
19 ♀Q♂.
20 ☿△♂. ☿⚺♃.
21 ☉⚺♇. ♄∠♆.
22 ☿⊥♇.
23 ☉∠♀. ☿⚹♄.
24 ☉△♂. ♀P♂.
25 ☉⚺♃. ☿⊥♃.
27 ☉⊥♇.
28 ☿∠♇.
29 ☉⚹♄.
30 ☿⚻♂. ♀⚹♆.
31 ☿∠♃.

LAST QUARTER-Dec.25, 7h. 6m. pm. (3° ♎ 46′)

JANUARY / FEBRUARY

D	☉	☽	☽Dec.	☿	♀	♂	D	☉	☽	☽Dec.	☿	♀	♂
1	1 01 08	13 57 55	4 55	1 36	1 15	46	1	1 00 52	14 13 58	4 16	1 18	1 15	47
2	1 01 09	14 03 22	5 07	1 37	1 15	46	2	1 00 52	14 04 15	3 23	1 13	1 15	47
3	1 01 09	14 06 29	5 03	1 37	1 15	46	3	1 00 51	13 53 59	2 18	1 07	1 15	47
4	1 01 09	14 07 48	4 42	1 37	1 15	46	4	1 00 50	13 43 54	1 04	1 00	1 15	47
5	1 01 09	14 07 42	4 04	1 38	1 15	46	5	1 00 49	13 34 10	0 12	0 52	1 15	47
6	1 01 10	14 06 16	3 10	1 38	1 15	46	6	1 00 48	13 24 30	1 24	0 44	1 15	47
7	1 01 10	14 03 14	2 02	1 39	1 15	46	7	1 00 47	13 14 24	2 27	0 34	1 15	47
8	1 01 10	13 58 08	0 44	1 39	1 15	46	8	1 00 46	13 03 27	3 17	0 25	1 15	47
9	1 01 10	13 50 22	0 36	1 39	1 15	46	9	1 00 45	12 51 25	3 53	0 14	1 15	47
10	1 01 10	13 39 37	1 49	1 40	1 15	46	10	1 00 43	12 38 29	4 16	0 04	1 15	47
11	1 01 09	13 25 53	2 51	1 40	1 15	46	11	1 00 42	12 25 14	4 25	0 07	1 15	47
12	1 01 09	13 09 44	3 37	1 40	1 15	46	12	1 00 40	12 12 30	4 24	0 18	1 15	47
13	1 01 08	12 52 11	4 07	1 41	1 15	46	13	1 00 39	12 01 21	4 13	0 28	1 15	47
14	1 01 08	12 34 33	4 23	1 41	1 15	46	14	1 00 37	11 52 54	3 54	0 37	1 15	47
15	1 01 07	12 18 15	4 28	1 41	1 15	46	15	1 00 36	11 48 09	3 26	0 46	1 15	47
16	1 01 06	12 04 37	4 22	1 42	1 15	46	16	1 00 34	11 47 58	2 51	0 53	1 15	47
17	1 01 06	11 54 47	4 08	1 42	1 15	46	17	1 00 32	11 52 59	2 08	0 59	1 15	47
18	1 01 05	11 49 36	3 46	1 42	1 15	46	18	1 00 30	12 03 34	1 17	1 04	1 15	47
19	1 01 04	11 49 37	3 17	1 42	1 15	46	19	1 00 29	12 19 42	0 19	1 06	1 15	47
20	1 01 03	11 55 03	2 39	1 42	1 15	46	20	1 00 27	12 40 55	0 45	1 07	1 15	47
21	1 01 02	12 05 51	1 52	1 42	1 15	46	21	1 00 25	13 06 09	1 51	1 06	1 15	47
22	1 01 01	12 21 31	0 56	1 41	1 15	47	22	1 00 23	13 33 35	2 56	1 04	1 15	47
23	1 01 00	12 41 10	0 07	1 40	1 15	47	23	1 00 21	14 00 45	3 54	1 00	1 15	47
24	1 00 59	13 03 26	1 15	1 40	1 15	47	24	1 00 19	14 24 43	4 40	0 55	1 15	47
25	1 00 58	13 26 28	2 23	1 38	1 15	47	25	1 00 18	14 42 34	5 10	0 50	1 15	47
26	1 00 57	13 48 09	3 25	1 37	1 15	47	26	1 00 16	14 52 14	5 20	0 43	1 15	47
27	1 00 56	14 06 16	4 17	1 35	1 15	47	27	1 00 14	14 53 00	5 08	0 36	1 15	47
28	1 00 56	14 19 07	4 53	1 33	1 15	47	28	1 00 13	14 45 40	4 36	0 29	1 15	47
29	1 00 55	14 25 46	5 12	1 30	1 15	47							
30	1 00 54	14 26 20	5 12	1 27	1 15	47							
31	1 00 53	14 21 53	4 52	1 23	1 15	47							

MARCH / APRIL

D	☉	☽	☽Dec.	☿	♀	♂	D	☉	☽	☽Dec.	☿	♀	♂
1	1 00 11	14 32 14	3 44	0 22	1 15	47	1	0 59 11	13 46 24	0 49	1 28	1 14	47
2	1 00 10	14 15 12	2 37	0 15	1 15	47	2	0 59 09	13 23 37	1 56	1 29	1 14	47
3	1 00 08	13 56 52	1 23	0 08	1 15	47	3	0 59 08	13 03 05	2 50	1 31	1 14	47
4	1 00 07	13 38 59	0 06	0 02	1 15	47	4	0 59 06	12 45 20	3 29	1 32	1 14	47
5	1 00 05	13 22 31	1 07	0 05	1 15	47	5	0 59 04	12 30 27	3 56	1 34	1 14	47
6	1 00 04	13 07 50	2 10	0 11	1 15	47	6	0 59 02	12 18 13	4 12	1 35	1 14	47
7	1 00 02	12 54 49	3 01	0 17	1 15	47	7	0 59 00	12 08 19	4 17	1 37	1 14	47
8	1 00 00	12 43 01	3 39	0 22	1 15	47	8	0 58 58	12 00 26	4 13	1 38	1 14	47
9	0 59 58	12 32 08	4 05	0 27	1 15	47	9	0 58 56	11 54 21	4 00	1 40	1 14	47
10	0 59 57	12 21 51	4 18	0 32	1 15	47	10	0 58 54	11 50 04	3 38	1 42	1 14	47
11	0 59 55	12 12 07	4 21	0 36	1 15	47	11	0 58 52	11 47 40	3 08	1 43	1 14	47
12	0 59 53	12 03 11	4 14	0 40	1 15	47	12	0 58 50	11 47 30	2 29	1 45	1 14	47
13	0 59 51	11 55 31	3 58	0 44	1 15	47	13	0 58 48	11 49 59	1 43	1 46	1 14	47
14	0 59 49	11 49 49	3 33	0 48	1 15	47	14	0 58 46	11 55 37	0 51	1 48	1 14	47
15	0 59 47	11 46 51	3 00	0 51	1 15	47	15	0 58 44	12 04 56	0 06	1 49	1 14	47
16	0 59 44	11 47 25	2 19	0 54	1 14	47	16	0 58 42	12 18 21	1 05	1 51	1 13	47
17	0 59 42	11 52 14	1 31	0 57	1 14	47	17	0 58 40	12 36 04	2 04	1 52	1 13	47
18	0 59 40	12 02 02	0 37	1 00	1 14	47	18	0 58 37	12 57 55	2 59	1 54	1 13	47
19	0 59 38	12 17 00	0 22	1 02	1 14	47	19	0 58 35	13 23 13	3 48	1 56	1 13	46
20	0 59 36	12 37 11	1 24	1 05	1 14	47	20	0 58 33	13 50 39	4 29	1 57	1 13	46
21	0 59 33	13 02 00	2 25	1 07	1 14	47	21	0 58 31	14 18 04	4 58	1 59	1 13	46
22	0 59 31	13 30 12	3 23	1 10	1 14	47	22	0 58 28	14 42 46	5 11	2 00	1 13	46
23	0 59 29	13 59 40	4 14	1 12	1 14	47	23	0 58 26	15 01 47	5 04	2 02	1 13	46
24	0 59 26	14 27 34	4 53	1 14	1 14	47	24	0 58 25	15 12 31	4 33	2 03	1 13	46
25	0 59 24	14 50 36	5 15	1 16	1 14	47	25	0 58 23	15 13 30	3 40	2 04	1 13	46
26	0 59 22	15 05 47	5 17	1 18	1 14	47	26	0 58 21	15 04 43	2 26	2 06	1 13	46
27	0 59 20	15 11 09	4 56	1 19	1 14	47	27	0 58 19	14 47 39	1 02	2 07	1 13	46
28	0 59 18	15 06 26	4 11	1 21	1 14	47	28	0 58 18	14 24 40	0 23	2 08	1 13	46
29	0 59 16	14 53 00	3 07	1 23	1 14	47	29	0 58 16	13 58 43	1 39	2 09	1 13	46
30	0 59 15	14 33 19	1 50	1 24	1 14	47	30	0 58 15	13 32 14	2 39	2 09	1 13	46
31	0 59 13	14 10 16	0 28	1 26	1 14	47							

MAY / JUNE

D	☉	☽	☽Dec.	☿	♀	♂	D	☉	☽	☽Dec.	☿	♀	♂
1	0 58 13	13 07 14	3 24	2 10	1 13	46	1	0 57 30	12 10 58	4 18	0 47	1 11	45
2	0 58 12	12 45 04	3 53	2 10	1 13	46	2	0 57 29	11 58 33	4 07	0 43	1 11	45
3	0 58 10	12 26 29	4 10	2 10	1 13	46	3	0 57 28	11 50 45	3 49	0 39	1 11	44
4	0 58 09	12 11 44	4 16	2 09	1 13	46	4	0 57 27	11 47 18	3 23	0 35	1 11	44
5	0 58 07	12 00 45	4 13	2 08	1 13	46	5	0 57 27	11 47 47	2 50	0 30	1 11	44
6	0 58 06	11 53 16	4 02	2 07	1 13	46	6	0 57 26	11 51 40	2 08	0 26	1 11	44
7	0 58 04	11 48 56	3 43	2 06	1 13	46	7	0 57 25	11 58 22	1 18	0 22	1 11	44
8	0 58 03	11 47 22	3 15	2 05	1 13	46	8	0 57 24	12 07 19	0 23	0 17	1 11	44
9	0 58 01	11 48 16	2 39	2 03	1 13	46	9	0 57 24	12 17 58	0 36	0 13	1 11	44
10	0 58 00	11 51 27	1 55	2 01	1 13	46	10	0 57 23	12 29 54	1 35	0 08	1 11	44
11	0 57 58	11 56 48	1 03	1 58	1 12	46	11	0 57 22	12 42 48	2 31	0 03	1 11	44
12	0 57 57	12 04 22	0 07	1 56	1 12	46	12	0 57 21	12 56 28	3 20	0 01	1 11	44
13	0 57 55	12 14 19	0 51	1 53	1 12	46	13	0 57 20	13 10 51	4 01	0 06	1 11	44
14	0 57 53	12 26 48	1 49	1 50	1 12	46	14	0 57 19	13 25 51	4 31	0 10	1 11	44
15	0 57 51	12 42 00	2 43	1 47	1 12	45	15	0 57 18	13 41 21	4 48	0 14	1 10	44
16	0 57 50	12 59 54	3 31	1 44	1 12	45	16	0 57 17	13 57 00	4 52	0 18	1 10	44
17	0 57 48	13 20 15	4 11	1 41	1 12	45	17	0 57 16	14 12 09	4 40	0 22	1 10	44
18	0 57 46	13 42 23	4 41	1 38	1 12	45	18	0 57 16	14 25 44	4 10	0 25	1 10	44
19	0 57 45	14 05 09	4 58	1 35	1 12	45	19	0 57 15	14 36 21	3 20	0 28	1 10	44
20	0 57 43	14 26 49	4 59	1 31	1 12	45	20	0 57 14	14 42 26	2 12	0 30	1 10	43
21	0 57 41	14 45 15	4 41	1 28	1 12	45	21	0 57 14	14 42 36	0 51	0 32	1 10	43
22	0 57 40	14 58 11	4 01	1 24	1 12	45	22	0 57 13	14 36 00	0 33	0 34	1 10	43
23	0 57 39	15 03 42	3 00	1 21	1 12	45	23	0 57 13	14 22 38	1 52	0 35	1 10	43
24	0 57 37	15 00 42	1 41	1 18	1 12	45	24	0 57 13	14 03 34	2 56	0 35	1 10	43
25	0 57 36	14 49 12	0 14	1 14	1 12	45	25	0 57 12	13 40 36	3 42	0 35	1 10	43
26	0 57 35	14 30 28	1 10	1 10	1 12	45	26	0 57 12	13 15 57	4 10	0 34	1 09	43
27	0 57 34	14 06 39	2 21	1 07	1 12	45	27	0 57 12	12 51 50	4 23	0 32	1 09	43
28	0 57 33	13 40 16	3 15	1 03	1 12	45	28	0 57 12	12 30 07	4 24	0 30	1 09	43
29	0 57 32	13 13 47	3 51	0 59	1 12	45	29	0 57 12	12 12 11	4 15	0 28	1 09	43
30	0 57 31	12 49 12	4 11	0 55	1 11	45	30	0 57 12	11 58 57	3 58	0 25	1 09	43
31	0 57 30	12 27 58	4 19	0 51	1 11	45							

JULY / AUGUST

D	☉	☽	☽Dec.	☿	♀	♂	D	☉	☽	☽Dec.	☿	♀	♂
1	0 57 13	11 50 49	3 33	0 21	1 09	43	1	0 57 25	11 59 20	1 01	1 57	1 04	41
2	0 57 13	11 47 50	3 01	0 17	1 09	43	2	0 57 26	12 12 02	0 05	1 59	1 04	40
3	0 57 13	11 49 47	2 22	0 13	1 09	43	3	0 57 28	12 28 29	0 55	2 01	1 04	40
4	0 57 13	11 56 09	1 35	0 09	1 09	43	4	0 57 29	12 47 21	1 55	2 02	1 04	40
5	0 57 13	12 06 13	0 42	0 04	1 09	43	5	0 57 30	13 07 07	2 52	2 03	1 04	40
6	0 57 14	12 19 05	0 17	0 01	1 08	42	6	0 57 31	13 26 03	3 41	2 04	1 03	40
7	0 57 14	12 33 44	1 18	0 06	1 08	42	7	0 57 32	13 42 35	4 20	2 04	1 03	40
8	0 57 14	12 49 05	2 16	0 11	1 08	42	8	0 57 33	13 55 32	4 45	2 04	1 03	40
9	0 57 14	13 04 08	3 09	0 16	1 08	42	9	0 57 34	14 04 19	4 55	2 04	1 03	40
10	0 57 14	13 18 06	3 53	0 21	1 08	42	10	0 57 35	14 09 09	4 47	2 04	1 02	40
11	0 57 14	13 30 29	4 26	0 27	1 08	42	11	0 57 35	14 10 36	4 23	2 03	1 02	40
12	0 57 14	13 41 11	4 46	0 32	1 08	42	12	0 57 36	14 09 45	3 42	2 02	1 02	40
13	0 57 14	13 50 22	4 51	0 37	1 08	42	13	0 57 37	14 07 27	2 45	2 01	1 02	40
14	0 57 14	13 58 22	4 41	0 42	1 08	42	14	0 57 38	14 04 13	1 37	2 00	1 01	39
15	0 57 14	14 05 25	4 14	0 47	1 07	42	15	0 57 39	14 00 09	0 21	1 59	1 01	39
16	0 57 14	14 11 29	3 31	0 53	1 07	42	16	0 57 40	13 54 52	0 54	1 58	1 01	39
17	0 57 14	14 16 10	2 31	0 58	1 07	42	17	0 57 41	13 47 48	2 03	1 56	1 00	39
18	0 57 15	14 18 39	1 19	1 03	1 07	42	18	0 57 42	13 38 22	3 00	1 55	1 00	39
19	0 57 15	14 17 54	0 01	1 07	1 07	41	19	0 57 44	13 26 18	3 43	1 54	1 00	39
20	0 57 15	14 12 55	1 20	1 12	1 07	41	20	0 57 45	13 11 47	4 10	1 52	0 59	39
21	0 57 16	14 03 08	2 29	1 17	1 06	41	21	0 57 46	12 55 31	4 23	1 51	0 59	39
22	0 57 16	13 48 40	3 23	1 22	1 06	41	22	0 57 48	12 38 35	4 24	1 50	0 58	39
23	0 57 17	13 30 22	4 00	1 26	1 06	41	23	0 57 49	12 22 18	4 13	1 48	0 58	39
24	0 57 17	13 09 45	4 21	1 30	1 06	41	24	0 57 51	12 07 59	3 53	1 47	0 58	39
25	0 57 18	12 48 36	4 27	1 35	1 06	41	25	0 57 53	11 56 51	3 24	1 45	0 57	38
26	0 57 19	12 28 46	4 22	1 39	1 06	41	26	0 57 54	11 49 53	2 49	1 44	0 57	38
27	0 57 20	12 11 48	4 07	1 42	1 05	41	27	0 57 56	11 47 50	2 07	1 43	0 56	38
28	0 57 21	11 58 56	3 44	1 46	1 05	41	28	0 57 58	11 51 06	1 19	1 42	0 56	38
29	0 57 22	11 50 59	3 13	1 49	1 05	41	29	0 58 00	11 59 50	0 26	1 40	0 55	38
30	0 57 23	11 48 24	2 36	1 52	1 05	41	30	0 58 02	12 13 50	0 31	1 39	0 55	38
31	0 57 24	11 51 15	1 52	1 55	1 05	41	31	0 58 04	12 32 25	1 30	1 38	0 54	38

28					DAILY MOTIONS OF THE PLANETS, 1994						

SEPTEMBER / OCTOBER

D	☉	☽	☽Dec.	☿	♀	♂	D	☉	☽	☽Dec.	☿	♀	♂
1	0 58 06	12 54 29	2 27	1 36	0 54	38	1	0 59 02	13 46 33	4 21	0 41	0 23	34
2	0 58 07	13 18 23	3 20	1 35	0 53	38	2	0 59 04	14 12 15	4 48	0 36	0 21	34
3	0 58 09	13 42 01	4 05	1 34	0 53	38	3	0 59 06	14 33 59	4 59	0 32	0 20	34
4	0 58 11	14 03 06	4 38	1 33	0 52	38	4	0 59 09	14 49 20	4 50	0 27	0 18	34
5	0 58 13	14 19 33	4 56	1 32	0 52	37	5	0 59 11	14 56 42	4 20	0 21	0 16	34
6	0 58 14	14 29 57	4 56	1 30	0 51	37	6	0 59 13	14 55 42	3 28	0 15	0 14	34
7	0 58 16	14 33 50	4 37	1 29	0 50	37	7	0 59 14	14 47 12	2 20	0 09	0 12	33
8	0 58 18	14 31 46	3 58	1 28	0 50	37	8	0 59 16	14 32 56	1 02	0 02	0 10	33
9	0 58 19	14 25 04	3 03	1 27	0 49	37	9	0 59 18	14 15 01	0 18	0 05	0 07	33
10	0 58 21	14 15 17	1 54	1 25	0 48	37	10	0 59 20	13 55 26	1 30	0 13	0 05	33
11	0 58 22	14 03 52	0 39	1 24	0 47	37	11	0 59 22	13 35 48	2 30	0 21	0 03	33
12	0 58 24	13 51 50	0 36	1 23	0 46	37	12	0 59 23	13 17 10	3 16	0 29	0 01	33
13	0 58 25	13 39 44	1 45	1 21	0 46	37	13	0 59 25	13 00 07	3 48	0 38	0 02	32
14	0 58 27	13 27 39	2 42	1 20	0 45	36	14	0 59 27	12 44 52	4 07	0 46	0 04	32
15	0 58 29	13 15 30	3 27	1 19	0 44	36	15	0 59 29	12 31 24	4 15	0 54	0 07	32
16	0 58 30	13 03 02	3 57	1 17	0 43	36	16	0 59 30	12 19 38	4 12	1 01	0 09	32
17	0 58 32	12 50 12	4 15	1 16	0 42	36	17	0 59 32	12 09 28	3 59	1 07	0 12	32
18	0 58 34	12 37 07	4 20	1 14	0 41	36	18	0 59 34	12 00 56	3 38	1 11	0 14	32
19	0 58 36	12 24 10	4 14	1 12	0 40	36	19	0 59 36	11 54 08	3 08	1 14	0 16	31
20	0 58 38	12 11 59	3 58	1 11	0 39	36	20	0 59 38	11 49 23	2 30	1 15	0 19	31
21	0 58 40	12 01 19	3 32	1 09	0 37	36	21	0 59 41	11 47 02	1 46	1 13	0 21	31
22	0 58 42	11 53 02	2 59	1 07	0 36	35	22	0 59 43	11 47 34	0 56	1 09	0 23	31
23	0 58 44	11 47 58	2 19	1 05	0 35	35	23	0 59 45	11 51 29	0 03	1 04	0 25	31
24	0 58 46	11 46 50	1 33	1 02	0 34	35	24	0 59 47	11 59 16	0 51	0 56	0 27	30
25	0 58 49	11 50 17	0 42	1 00	0 32	35	25	0 59 49	12 11 17	1 44	0 46	0 29	30
26	0 58 51	11 58 43	0 12	0 57	0 31	35	26	0 59 51	12 27 43	2 34	0 36	0 31	30
27	0 58 53	12 12 19	1 07	0 54	0 30	35	27	0 59 54	12 48 25	3 20	0 25	0 32	30
28	0 58 55	12 30 51	2 03	0 51	0 28	35	28	0 59 56	13 12 48	3 59	0 13	0 33	30
29	0 58 58	12 53 41	2 55	0 48	0 26	35	29	0 59 58	13 39 39	4 30	0 02	0 34	29
30	0 59 00	13 19 33	3 42	0 45	0 25	34	30	1 00 00	14 07 07	4 49	0 09	0 35	29
							31	1 00 02	14 32 43	4 52	0 20	0 36	29

NOVEMBER / DECEMBER

D	☉	☽	☽Dec.	☿	♀	♂	D	☉	☽	☽Dec.	☿	♀	♂
1	1 00 04	14 53 39	4 35	0 30	0 36	29	1	1 00 51	15 10 31	2 16	1 34	0 19	19
2	1 00 06	15 07 18	3 55	0 39	0 36	28	2	1 00 53	15 12 12	0 53	1 34	0 21	19
3	1 00 08	15 11 52	2 54	0 47	0 36	28	3	1 00 54	15 03 53	0 34	1 34	0 22	18
4	1 00 10	15 06 50	1 36	0 54	0 36	28	4	1 00 55	14 46 29	1 53	1 34	0 24	18
5	1 00 12	14 53 05	0 12	1 00	0 35	28	5	1 00 55	14 22 16	2 57	1 34	0 26	17
6	1 00 13	14 32 43	1 09	1 06	0 35	27	6	1 00 56	13 54 17	3 41	1 34	0 28	17
7	1 00 15	14 08 20	2 18	1 11	0 34	27	7	1 00 57	13 25 32	4 07	1 34	0 29	16
8	1 00 16	13 42 35	3 09	1 15	0 32	27	8	1 00 58	12 58 32	4 18	1 34	0 31	16
9	1 00 18	13 17 36	3 45	1 18	0 31	27	9	1 00 58	12 35 02	4 18	1 34	0 33	15
10	1 00 19	12 54 55	4 05	1 21	0 29	26	10	1 00 59	12 16 02	4 07	1 34	0 34	15
11	1 00 20	12 35 28	4 14	1 24	0 27	26	11	1 00 59	12 01 54	3 49	1 34	0 35	14
12	1 00 22	12 19 35	4 12	1 26	0 26	26	12	1 01 00	11 52 35	3 23	1 34	0 37	14
13	1 00 23	12 06 49	4 01	1 28	0 23	25	13	1 01 01	11 47 42	2 50	1 34	0 38	13
14	1 00 25	11 58 16	3 42	1 29	0 21	25	14	1 01 01	11 46 41	2 10	1 35	0 39	13
15	1 00 26	11 52 15	3 15	1 30	0 19	25	15	1 01 02	11 48 52	1 24	1 35	0 41	12
16	1 00 28	11 48 52	2 40	1 31	0 17	25	16	1 01 02	11 53 37	0 33	1 35	0 42	12
17	1 00 29	11 47 47	1 58	1 32	0 14	24	17	1 01 03	12 00 18	0 22	1 35	0 43	11
18	1 00 31	11 48 51	1 09	1 33	0 12	24	18	1 01 04	12 08 26	1 16	1 35	0 44	10
19	1 00 33	11 52 01	0 17	1 33	0 09	24	19	1 01 04	12 17 42	2 07	1 35	0 45	10
20	1 00 34	11 57 21	0 37	1 34	0 07	23	20	1 01 05	12 28 02	2 54	1 35	0 46	9
21	1 00 36	12 05 07	1 30	1 34	0 04	23	21	1 01 06	12 39 31	3 33	1 36	0 47	8
22	1 00 37	12 15 36	2 20	1 34	0 02	23	22	1 01 06	12 52 24	4 03	1 36	0 48	8
23	1 00 39	12 29 06	3 04	1 34	0 01	22	23	1 01 07	13 07 00	4 24	1 36	0 49	7
24	1 00 41	12 45 51	3 43	1 34	0 03	22	24	1 01 08	13 23 31	4 34	1 36	0 50	7
25	1 00 42	13 05 48	4 13	1 34	0 06	22	25	1 01 08	13 41 49	4 31	1 36	0 51	6
26	1 00 44	13 28 34	4 34	1 34	0 08	21	26	1 01 09	14 01 21	4 13	1 37	0 51	5
27	1 00 45	13 53 14	4 43	1 34	0 10	21	27	1 01 09	14 20 51	3 37	1 37	0 52	4
28	1 00 47	14 18 11	4 36	1 34	0 12	20	28	1 01 10	14 38 27	2 43	1 37	0 53	4
29	1 00 49	14 41 10	4 11	1 34	0 15	20	29	1 01 11	14 51 43	1 31	1 37	0 53	3
30	1 00 50	14 59 31	3 24	1 34	0 17	20	30	1 01 11	14 58 14	0 09	1 37	0 54	2
							31	1 01 11	14 56 09	1 15	1 37	0 55	1

D.M.		JANUARY
2	6.00 A.M.	⊕ in Perihelion.
3	3.49 A.M.	☽ on Equator.
3	8.20 P.M.	☿ Sup. ☌ ☉.
6	1.16 A.M.	☽ in Perigee.
9	1.07 P.M.	☽ Max. Dec. 21° S. 30′.
16	10.12 A.M.	☽ on Equator.
17	2.04 A.M.	♀ Sup. ☌ ☉.
19	5.15 A.M.	☽ in Apogee.
23	9.32 P.M.	☽ Max. Dec. 21° N. 26′.
26	6.50 A.M.	♀ in Aphelion.
30	11.06 A.M.	☽ on Equator.
31	3.43 A.M.	☽ in Perigee.

		FEBRUARY
2	8.50 P.M.	☿ in ☊.
4	9.00 P.M.	☿ Gt. Elong. 18° E.
5	8.05 P.M.	☽ Max. Dec. 21° S. 20′.
7	0.31 P.M.	☿ in Perihelion.
12	7.16 P.M.	☽ on Equator.
16	1.35 A.M.	☽ In Apogee.
20	7.15 A.M.	☽ Max. Dec. 21° N. 12′.
20	8.01 A.M.	☿ Inf. ☌ ☉.
26	8.39 P.M.	☽ on Equator.
27	10.08 P.M.	☽ in Perigee.

		MARCH
5	1.46 A.M.	☽ Max. Dec. 21° S. 5′.
12	2.37 A.M.	☽ on Equator.
13	4.03 A.M.	☿ in ☋.
15	5.12 P.M.	☽ in Apogee.
19	2.00 A.M.	☿ Gt. Elong. 28° W.
19	3.16 P.M.	☽ Max. Dec. 20° N. 56′.
20	8.28 P.M.	☉ Enters ♈, Equinox.
23	0.09 P.M.	☿ in Aphelion.
26	7.25 A.M.	☽ on Equator.
28	6.13 A.M.	☽ in Perigee.

		APRIL
1	8.21 A.M.	☽ Max. Dec. 20° S. 51′.
4	3.48 P.M.	♂ in Perihelion.
8	8.18 A.M.	☽ on Equator.
11	11.49 P.M.	☽ in Apogee.
14	9.07 P.M.	♀ in ☊.
15	9.27 P.M.	☽ Max. Dec. 20° N. 46′.
22	5.38 P.M.	☽ on Equator.
25	5.17 P.M.	☽ in Perigee.
28	5.10 P.M.	☽ Max. Dec. 20° S. 44′.
30	10.21 A.M.	☿ Sup. ☌ ☉.

		MAY
1	8.06 P.M.	☿ in ☊.
5	1.44 P.M.	☽ on Equator.
6	11.46 A.M.	☿ in Perihelion.
9	2.18 A.M.	☽ in Apogee.
10	5.07 P.M.	● Annular Eclipse.
13	3.02 A.M.	☽ Max. Dec. 20° N. 44′.
18	4.22 P.M.	♀ In Perihelion.
20	2.07 A.M.	☽ on Equator.
24	2.55 A.M.	☽ in Perigee.
25	3.39 A.M.	☽ Partial Eclipse
26	3.44 A.M.	☽ Max. Dec. 20° S. 44′.
30	7.00 A.M.	☿ Gt. Elong. 23° E.

		JUNE
1	8.29 P.M.	☽ on Equator.
5	0.38 P.M.	☽ in Apogee.
9	3.18 A.M.	☿ in ☋.
9	9.25 A.M.	☽ Max. Dec. 20° N. 45′.
16	8.53 A.M.	☽ on Equator.
19	11.24 A.M.	☿ in Aphelion.
21	6.43 A.M.	☽ in Perigee.
21	2.48 P.M.	☉ Enters ♋, Solstice.
22	2.26 P.M.	☽ Max. Dec. 20° S. 45′.
25	9.57 A.M.	☿ Inf. ☌ ☉.
29	5.05 A.M.	☽ on Equator.

D.M.		JULY
3	4.40 A.M.	☽ in Apogee.
5	7.00 P.M.	⊕ in Aphelion.
6	5.13 P.M.	☽ Max. Dec. 20° N. 43′.
13	3.03 P.M.	☽ on Equator.
17	2.00 P.M.	☿ Gt. Elong. 21° W.
18	5.31 P.M.	☽ in Perigee.
19	11.39 P.M.	☽ Max. Dec. 20° S. 40′.
26	2.44 P.M.	☽ on Equator.
28	7.21 P.M.	☿ in ☊.
30	10.56 P.M.	☽ in Apogee.

		AUGUST
2	11.02 A.M.	☿ in Perihelion.
3	2.05 A.M.	☽ Max. Dec. 20° N. 35′.
3	5.13 P.M.	♂ in ☊.
4	10.25 A.M.	♀ in ☋.
9	10.01 P.M.	☽ on Equator.
12	11.10 P.M.	☽ in Perigee.
13	0.54 A.M.	☿ Sup. ☌ ☉.
16	6.40 A.M.	☽ Max. Dec. 20° S. 29′.
22	11.57 P.M.	☽ on Equator.
24	11.00 P.M.	♀ Gt. Elong. 46° E.
27	5.52 P.M.	☽ in Apogee
30	10.59 A.M.	☽ Max. Dec. 20° N. 21′.

		SEPTEMBER
5	2.34 A.M.	☿ in ☋.
6	6.36 A.M.	☽ on Equator.
8	0.55 A.M.	♀ in Aphelion.
8	2.23 P.M.	☽ in Perigee.
12	0.15 P.M.	☽ Max. Dec. 20° S. 15′.
15	10.40 A.M.	☿ in Aphelion.
19	7.35 A.M.	☽ on Equator.
23	6.19 A.M.	☉ Enters ♎, Equinox.
24	0.03 P.M.	☽ in Apogee.
26	4.00 P.M.	☿ Gt. Elong. 26° E.
26	6.53 P.M.	☽ Max. Dec. 20° N. 8′.
28	10.00 P.M.	♀ Gt. Brilliance.

		OCTOBER
3	4.37 P.M.	☽ on Equator.
6	2.06 P.M.	☽ in Perigee.
9	6.28 P.M.	☽ Max. Dec. 20° S. 4′.
16	1.30 P.M.	☽ on Equator.
21	5.17 A.M.	☿ Inf. ☌ ☉.
22	1.52 A.M.	☽ in Apogee.
24	1.31 A.M.	☽ Max. Dec. 20° N. 1′.
24	6.37 P.M.	☿ in ☊.
29	10.17 A.M.	☿ in Perihelion.
31	2.53 P.M.	☽ on Equator.

		NOVEMBER
2	11.12 P.M.	♀ Inf. ☌ ☉.
3	1.35 P.M.	● Total Eclipse.
3	11.39 P.M.	☽ in Perigee.
6	1.00 A.M.	☿ Gt. Elong. 19° W.
6	3.13 A.M.	☽ Max. Dec. 20° S. 0′.
12	7.01 P.M.	☽ on Equator.
18	5.08 A.M.	☽ in Apogee.
20	7.42 A.M.	☽ Max. Dec. 20° N. 1′.
25	1.52 P.M.	♀ in ☊.
27	0.01 P.M.	☽ on Equator.

		DECEMBER
2	1.50 A.M.	☿ in ☋.
2	0.19 P.M.	☽ in Perigee.
3	2.33 P.M.	☽ Max. Dec. 20° S. 2′.
9	11.00 A.M.	♀ Gt. Brilliance.
10	2.01 A.M.	☽ on Equator.
12	9.55 A.M.	☿ in Aphelion.
14	3.16 A.M.	☿ Sup. ☌ ☉.
15	7.47 A.M.	☽ in Apogee.
17	2.34 P.M.	☽ Max. Dec. 20° N. 3′.
22	2.23 A.M.	☉ Enters ♑, Solstice.
24	7.25 P.M.	☽ on Equator.
29	8.56 A.M.	♀ in Perihelion.
30	11.04 P.M.	☽ in Perigee.
31	2.28 A.M.	☽ Max. Dec. 20° S. 1′.

Showing the approximate time when each Aspect is formed.
am denotes morning; pm denotes afternoon.
Note:- Semi-quintile, or 36° apart, ⊥; Bi-quintile, or 144° ±; Quincunx or 150° ⊽
☽ ☌ ● Eclipse of ☉. ☽ ☍ ☉ Eclipse of ☽. ☌ Occultation by ☽.

JANUARY

Day	Aspect	Time	
1 S	☽⚼♀	6am	7
	☽⚼☿	10	32
	☽⚼♂	10	36
	☿☌♂	11	37
	☽⚼☉	1pm	11
	☽☍♄	3	11
	☽□♇	3	14
	☿⚹♃	6	9
	☽P♇	10	55
2 SU	♄□♇	2am	55
	♂⚹♃	3	8
	☽⚼♆	5	42
	☽⚼♅	7	41
	☽△♀	10	30
	☽⚹♃	1pm	24
	☽△♂	1	52
	☽△☿	3	39
	☽△☉	4	57
	☉∠♇	6	11
	☉∠♄	7	16
3 M	☿∠♇	4am	0
	☿∠♄	5	6
	☽△♆	7	25
	☽△♅	9	25
	♃P♄	9	30
	☽∠♃	3pm	16
	☽⚹♇	6	41
	☉☌☿	8	20
	♀⚹♃	10	47
4 TU	☽P♇	8am	33
	☽⊻♃	5pm	3
	☽□♀	6	38
	☽□♂	7	54
	☽∠♇	8	14
	☽⚼♄	8	33
5 W	☽□☉	0am	1
	☽□☿	1	20
	♂∠♇	2	25
	♂∠♄	9	41
	☽□♆	10	34
	☽□♅	0pm	38
	♀∠♇	1	5
	♀∠♄	5	55
	☽⊻♇	9	46
	☽△♄	10	12
6 TH	☽P♄	0am	13
	☽P♃	1	27
	♀☌♂	5	1
	☽☌♃	8pm	32
7 F	☽⚹♂	1am	47
	☽⚹♀	2	35
	☽⚹☉	6	57
	☽⚹☿	10	59
	☽⚹♆	1pm	42
	☽⚹♅	3	52
8 S	☽☌♇	0am	56
	☽□♄	1	38
	☽∠♂	4	50
	☽∠♀	6	41
	☽∠☉	10	34
	☿☌♆	10	49

Day	Aspect	Time	
	☽∠♆	3pm	24
	☽∠☿	4	0
	☽∠♅	5	36
	☽P♆	9	52
9 SU	☽⊻♃	0am	18
	☿⊥♄	2	20
	☿☌♅	6	7
	☽⊻♂	8	4
	☽⊻♀	10	58
	☽⊻☉	2pm	22
	☉P♅	2	28
	☽⊻♆	5	17
	☽⊻♅	7	33
	☿Q♃	8	19
	☽⊻☿	9	18
10 M	☽∠♃	2am	27
	☽⊻♇	4	39
	☽P♆	4	40
	☽⚹♄	5	39
	☿P♂	1pm	15
11 TU	☽⚹♃	4am	56
	☽∠♇	6	57
	☉☌♆	7	33
	☽∠♄	8	8
	☽☌♂	3pm	32
	☽☌♀	8	46
	☽☌♆	10	2
	☽☌☉	11	10
12 W	☽☌♅	0am	27
	☽☌☿	9	31
	☽⚹♇	9	44
	♀☌♆	10	40
	☽⊻♄	11	5
	☿⚹♇	11	18
	☉⊥♄	2pm	43
	☉☌♅	4	59
	☿⊻♄	10	48
13 TH	☽P♃	2am	17
	☽P♄	7	7
	☿P♀	9	46
	☽□♃	11	27
	♀⊥♄	0pm	59
	♀☌♅	1	56
14 F	☉Q♃	0am	6
	☽⊻♂	1	28
	☽⊻♆	4	59
	☽⊻♅	7	37
	☽⊻♀	9	28
	☽⊻☉	10	47
	☿P♅	0pm	4
	♄⊥♅	0	45
	♀Q♃	3	44
	☽□♇	5	15
	☽☌♄	7	2
15 S	☉P♆	0am	31
	☽P♇	1	18
	☽⊻☿	1	24
	☽∠♂	7	43
	☽∠♆	9	34
	☽∠♅	0pm	19
	♀P♅	3	9
	☽∠♀	5	19
	☽∠☉	6	0

Day	Aspect	Time	
	☽△♃	8	50
16 SU	☽∠☿	11am	7
	☿P♆	2pm	2
	♂☌♆	2	53
	☽⚹♆	2	55
	☽⚹♂	2	55
	☽⚹♅	5	48
17 M	☉☌♀	2am	4
	☽⚹☉	2	11
	☽⚹♀	2	11
	☽⚼♃	2	40
	☽△♇	3	46
	☽⊻♄	6	3
	☉P☿	5pm	8
	♀⚹♇	5	32
	☽P♇	7	57
	☉⚹♇	9	15
	☽⚹☿	9	54
18 TU	☽⚼♇	9am	58
	☽∠♄	0pm	30
	♂☌♅	3	43
	♀⊻♄	6	19
	♂⊥♄	11	9
19 W	☽□♆	3am	23
	☉⊻♄	4	55
	☽□♅	6	27
	☽□♂	7	24
	♀P♆	0pm	43
	☽P♄	3	51
	☿Q♇	4	21
	☽⚹♄	7	14
	☽□☉	8	27
	☽□♀	9	57
20 TH	☽P♃	0am	39
	☽□☿	8pm	52
	☽☍♃	10	30
	♂Q♃	11	35
21 F	☿□♃	9am	3
	☽P☿	2pm	0
	☽△♆	4	13
	☽△♅	7	20
22 S	☽△♂	0am	7
	☽P☉	2	19
	☽☍♇	4	56
	☽□♄	8	5
	☽P♀	0pm	13
	☽△☉	2	10
	♂P♅	2	49
	☽△♀	5	2
	☽⚼♆	9	53
23 SU	☽⚼♅	0am	59
	☽P♆	4	20
	☽⚼♂	7	27
	☽△☿	5pm	26
	☽⚼☉	9	41
24 M	☽⚼♀	1am	7
	☽P♆	2pm	39
	☽⚼♃	2	51
	☽△♄	6	1
25 TU	☽⚼☿	1am	41
	♂⚹♇	5	18
	☽P♀	5pm	52
	☽⚼♇	6	6

Day	Aspect	Time	
	☽△♃	6	29
	☽⚼♄	9	34
26 W	☽P☉	1am	6
	☽☍♆	9	36
	☽☍♅	0pm	33
	☿⊻♆	5	59
	☽△♇	8	42
	☽☍♂	11	0
27 TH	☽P☿	4am	46
	☽P♃	9	11
	♀Q♇	10	44
	☽☍☉	1pm	23
	☽☍♀	6	6
	☿⊻♅	7	49
	☽P♄	7	53
	☽□♃	11	13
28 F	♂⊻♄	0am	39
	♂P♆	3	50
	☿P♃	4	42
	☽☍☿	6pm	42
	☽□♇	11	56
29 S	☽☍♄	3am	41
	☽P♇	6	51
	☽⚼♆	2pm	33
	☽⚼♅	5	27
	☉Q♇	10	29
30 SU	☽⚹♃	1am	52
	☽⚼♂	7	24
	♀□♃	7	29
	☽△♆	3pm	34
	☿⊥♆	5	3
	☽△♅	6	29
	☿□♇	9	0
	☽⚼☉	10	37
31 M	☿P♄	1am	0
	☽⚹♇	1	56
	☽∠♃	2	56
	☽⚼♀	4	39
	☽△♂	9	45
	☽P♇	3pm	16
	☿⊥♅	11	52

FEBRUARY

Day	Aspect	Time	
1 TU	☽△☉	1am	29
	☽∠♇	2	58
	☽⊻♃	4	5
	☽⚼☿	6	11
	☽⚼♄	7	14
	☽△♀	8	4
	☽□♆	5pm	44
	☿☌♄	6	26
	☽P☿	6	46
	☽□♅	8	46
2 W	☽P♄	0am	48
	☽⊻♇	4	11
	☽△♄	8	41
	☽△☿	9	59
	☽P♃	1pm	28
	☽□♂	3	1
	☉□♃	5	5
3 TH	☽P☉	2am	2
	☽P♀	2	23
	☽☌♃	7	6

Day	Aspect	Time	
	☽□☉	8	6
	☽□♀	3pm	54
	☉P♀	5	50
	☽⚹♆	8	55
4 F	☽⚹♅	0am	6
	☽☌♇	7	34
	☽P♂	7	40
	☽□♄	0pm	34
	☽□☿	6	9
	☽⚹♂	9	44
	☽∠♆	11	1
5 S	☽∠♅	2am	17
	☽P♆	4	47
	☽⊻♃	11	25
	☽⚹☉	4pm	21
6 SU	♀⊻♆	1am	9
	☽⊻♆	1	28
	☽⚹♀	1	30
	☽∠♂	1	42
	☽⊻♅	4	49
	☽P♆	11	46
	☽⊻♇	0pm	19
	☽∠♃	2	5
	☽⚹♄	5	52
	☽∠☉	9	8
7 M	☽⚹☿	2am	48
	☽⊻♂	6	6
	☽∠♀	6	59
	♀⊻♅	2pm	49
	☽∠♇	3	13
	☽⚹♃	5	7
	☽P♂	5	7
	♀P♃	6	19
	☽∠♄	9	4
8 TU	☽⊻☉	2am	22
	☽∠☿	7	13
	☽☌♆	7	26
	☽☌♅	10	58
	☽⊻♀	0pm	59
	☿∠♆	1	21
	☽⚹♇	6	30
	☉P♃	7	42
9 W	☽⊻♄	0am	40
	☽P♃	5	30
	☽P☉	6	33
	☽P♀	10	20
	☽⊻☿	11	40
	☽☌♂	4pm	18
	☽P♄	10	21
	♂Q♇	10	27
10 TH	☽□♃	0am	25
	☽☌☉	2pm	30
	☽⊻♆	3	8
	☽⊻♅	6	52
	☉⊻♆	10	39
	♀□♇	11	14
	♀⊥♆	11	14
11 F	☽□♇	2am	31
	☽☌♀	2	52
	☽P☿	7	3
	☿ Stat	8	30
	☽☌♄	9	25
	☽P♇	10	31

	☽∠♆	7pm	48
	☽☌☿	8	52
	☽∠♅	11	40
12 S	☽⊻♂	4am	57
	☽△♃	9	50
	♀⊥♅	2pm	54
13 SU	☉⊻♅	0am	17
	☽✱♆	1	5
	☽✱♅	5	5
	☽⊻☉	5	30
	☽∠♂	0pm	23
	☽△♇	0	51
	☽⚼♃	3	27
	☿∠♆	6	7
	☽⊻♀	7	55
	☽⊻♄	8	35
14 M	♀☌♄	2am	52
	♀P♄	4	12
	☽P♇	4	43
	☽P☿	6	4
	☽⊻☿	6	27
	☽∠☉	2pm	8
	☽⚼♇	6	52
	☽✱♂	8	30
15 TU	☽∠♄	3am	1
	☽∠♀	5	36
	☽∠☿	11	15
	☽□♆	1pm	19
	☽P♀	2	2
	♂□♃	2	17
	☽□♅	5	33
	☽P♄	5	48
	☽P☉	9	1
	☽✱☉	11	20
16 W	☽✱♄	9am	48
	☽P♃	2pm	41
	☽✱♀	3	42
	☽✱☿	3	52
	☿☌♀	4	44
	☉□♇	10	25
17 TH	☉⊥♆	1am	56
	☽P♂	8	56
	☽☍♃	10	45
	☉P♄	10	59
	☽□♂	1pm	46
18 F	☽△♆	2am	26
	☽△♅	6	44
	♀∠♆	8	21
	☽☍♇	2pm	10
	☽□☉	5	47
	☽□♄	11	6
	☽□☿	11	55
19 S	☉⊥♅	6am	38
	☿☌♄	8	3
	☽⚼♆	8	30
	☽□♀	11	12
	☽⚼♅	0pm	45
	☽P♆	4	35
20 SU	♀∠♅	2am	53
	☽△♂	5	36
	☉☌☿	8	1
	☽P♆	9pm	55
21 M	☽⚼♃	3am	39
	☿⊥♅	4	49
	☽△☿	5	19
	☽△☉	9	10
	☽△♄	9	43
	☽⚼♂	0pm	0
	☉☌♄	5	3

22 TU	☽△♀	2am	32
	☽⚼♇	4	37
	☽⚼☿	6	51
	☽△♃	7	25
	☿P♀	8	52
	☽⚼♄	1pm	28
	☽⚼☉	2	55
	☽☍♆	9	20
23 W	☽☍♅	1am	17
	☿⊥♆	3	15
	☽△♇	7	24
	☽⚼♀	8	6
	☿□♇	10	8
	☽P♂	11	50
	☽P♃	4pm	24
24 TH	♀△♃	6am	38
	☽□♃	11	52
	☽P♄	0pm	24
	☉P☿	5	39
	☽☍♂	11	50
25 F	☽P☿	0am	6
	☽P☉	1	19
	☽☍☿	7	14
	☽□♇	10	16
	☽P♀	1pm	37
	☽P♇	5	21
	☽☍♄	6	56
	♂⊻♆	8	22
26 S	☽☍☉	1am	15
	☽⚼♆	1	38
	♂P♃	3	30
	☽⚼♅	5	21
	☉∠♆	7	8
	☽✱♃	1pm	20
	☽☍♀	6	19
27 SU	☽△♆	1am	59
	☿⊻♅	2	48
	♀P♇	4	8
	☽△♅	5	41
	☽✱♇	11	0
	☽∠♃	1pm	33
	☽P♀	9	56
	☽P♇	11	37
28 M	☿☌♂	0am	59
	☽⚼☿	4	43
	☽⚼♂	5	5
	☽P☉	9	16
	☽∠♇	11	11
	☽⊻♃	1pm	44
	♃Stat	1	49
	☉∠♅	4	12
	☽⚼♄	8	18
	♂⊻♅	10	1
MARCH			
1 TU	☽P☿	0am	57
	☽□♆	2	32
	☽P♄	2	50
	☽△☿	4	12
	☽□♅	6	20
	☽△♂	6	46
	☽⚼☉	7	19
	♇Stat	10	1
	☽⊻♇	11	34
	☽P♂	5pm	23
	☽△♄	9	1
	☽P♃	11	3
	☿P♄	11	19
2	☽⚼♀	2am	2

W	☽△☉	9	51
	☽☌♃	2pm	57
	♀✱♆	3	32
	☿⊻♀	10	10
3 TH	☽✱♆	4am	18
	☽□☿	4	45
	☽△♀	5	30
	☽✱♅	8	19
	☽□♂	11	33
	☽☌♇	1pm	36
	☽□♄	11	54
4 F	☽∠♆	6am	0
	☽∠♅	10	9
	☽P♆	2pm	24
	♀✱♅	2	32
	☽□☉	4	53
	☽⊻♃	6	11
	☿⊻♆	7	3
5 S	♂□♇	0am	6
	☿Stat	5	50
	☽✱☿	8	16
	☽⊻♆	8	19
	☉△♃	10	30
	☽⊻♅	0pm	35
	☽P♆	1	24
	☽□♀	2	45
	☽⊻♇	5	57
	♂⊥♆	6	12
	☽✱♂	7	3
	☉P♇	7	47
	☽∠♃	8	42
6 SU	☿⊻♆	4am	33
	☽✱♄	5	14
	☽∠☿	11	17
	☽∠♇	9pm	1
	☿P♂	10	14
	☽✱♃	11	48
	☽∠♂	11	53
7 M	♀△♇	1am	8
	☽✱☉	2	57
	☽∠♄	8	48
	☽☌♆	2pm	43
	☽⊻☿	3	7
	☿⊥♀	6	16
	☽☌♅	7	15
8 TU	☽✱♇	0am	38
	☽✱♀	3	9
	☽⊻♂	5	22
	♀⚼♃	6	3
	☽∠☉	9	2
	☽P♃	10	12
	☽⊻♄	0pm	55
	♂⊥♅	11	50
9 W	☽P☿	0am	5
	☽P♂	5	54
	☽□♃	7	35
	☽∠♀	10	25
	☽P♄	11	31
	☽⊻☉	3pm	46
	☽⊻♆	11	16
10 TH	☽☌☿	1am	10
	☽⊻♅	4	1
	☽□♇	9	24
	♀⊻♂	1pm	34
	☽☌♂	6	10
	☽P♇	6	10
	☽⊻♀	6	21
	☽☌♄	10	41
11	☽∠♆	4am	16

F	☽P☉	5	44
	☽∠♅	9	9
	☽△♃	5pm	17
	☽P♀	11	32
12 S	☽P♀	6am	33
	☽☌☉	7	5
	☽✱♆	9	44
	♀Q♆	11	34
	☽⊻☿	2pm	23
	☽✱♅	2	44
	♀⊻♄	5	29
	☽△♇	8	4
	☽P☉	8	11
	☿⊻♅	9	33
	♂P♄	10	6
	☽⚼♃	10	49
13 SU	☽⊻♂	9am	17
	☽⊻♄	10	24
	☽P♇	11	30
	☽☌♀	0pm	10
	☉✱♆	4	12
	☽∠☿	10	9
14 M	☽⚼♇	2am	4
	♂☌♄	5	1
	♀Q♅	1pm	44
	☽P♂	3	38
	☽∠♄	4	54
	☽∠♂	5	37
	☽P♄	6	23
	☽□♆	10	0
15 TU	☽⊻☉	0am	41
	☽□♅	3	12
	☉P♀	5	16
	☽✱☿	6	35
	♀±♃	6	58
	☽P☿	7	34
	☽P♃	10pm	25
	☽✱♄	11	41
16 W	☽✱♂	2am	17
	☉✱♅	7	40
	☽⊻♀	8	3
	☿□♇	8	12
	☽∠☉	10	2
	☽☍♃	5pm	29
17 TH	☿⊥♆	9am	5
	☽△♆	11	10
	♂∠♆	1pm	18
	☽△♅	4	27
	☽∠♀	6	9
	☽✱☉	7	21
	☽☍♇	9	25
18 F	☽□☿	0am	33
	♀⊥♄	1	29
	☽□♄	1pm	12
	☽⚼♆	5	30
	☽□♂	7	26
	☉△♇	7	49
	☽⚼♅	10	45
19 S	♀⚼♇	1am	9
	☽✱♀	3	48
	☽P♆	7	29
	☽P♆	7pm	43
	☉⚼♃	10	6
	♀∇♃	10	16
20 SU	☿⊥♅	2am	37
	☽⚼♃	11	3
	☽□☉	0pm	14
	☽△☿	5	15
21	♂∠♅	0am	13

M	☽△♄	0	35
	☽△♂	9	46
	☽⚼♇	1pm	30
	☽△♃	3	23
	☽□♀	7	58
22 TU	☽⚼☿	0am	7
	☽⚼♄	4	48
	♀P♇	4	55
	☽☍♆	8	5
	☽☍♅	0pm	56
	☽⚼♂	3	8
	☽△♇	4	58
23 W	☽△☉	0am	29
	☽P♃	3	10
	♀⊥♂	5pm	41
	☽□♃	8	53
24 TH	☽P☿	2am	46
	☽P♄	4	32
	☽⚼☉	4	35
	☽△♀	6	32
	☿☌♄	9	58
	♃Q♅	2pm	20
	☽P♂	8	30
	☽□♇	8	46
	☽P♀	10	2
	♂△♃	10	40
25 F	☿P♄	3am	11
	☽P♇	4	46
	♀P♂	6	39
	☽⚼♀	9	54
	☽☍♄	11	7
	☽☍☿	1pm	12
	☽⚼♆	1	32
	☿∠♆	5	15
	☽⚼♅	5	58
	☽P☉	10	20
	☽✱♃	10	37
	☉Q♆	11	48
26 S	☽☍♂	0am	4
	♀∠♄	1	31
	♀±♇	5	53
	☽△♆	1pm	47
	☽P☉	5	52
	☽△♅	6	8
	☽✱♇	9	25
	☽∠♃	10	32
27 SU	♀□♆	5am	32
	☽P♇	9	24
	☽☍☉	11	10
	☽P♂	1pm	29
	☉⊻♄	6	40
	☿∠♅	8	59
	☽∠♇	9	9
	☽⊻♃	10	9
	☽P♀	11	2
28 M	☽P☿	2am	14
	☽P♄	7	28
	☉±♃	9	29
	☽⚼♄	11	29
	☽□♆	1pm	22
	☽☍♀	4	9
	☿P♀	5	38
	☽□♅	5	43
	☉Q♅	7	32
	☽⚼☿	7	41
	☽⊻♇	8	51
29 TU	☽⚼♂	3am	29
	☽P♃	6	30
	☽△♄	11	29

	♀□♅	11 44
	☿△♃	5pm 33
	☽☌♃	9 34
	☽△☿	10 0
30 W	☽△♂	4am 51
	♂P♇	0pm 26
	☽⚹♆	1 28
	☽⚼☉	4 1
	☽⚹♅	6 0
	☽☌♇	9 7
31 TH	♀⚻♇	1am 4
	♀P♄	6 30
	☽□♄	0pm 46
	☽∠♆	2 17
	☽△☉	6 42
	☽∠♅	6 57
	☽⊻♃	10 40
APRIL		
1 F	☽⚼♀	0am 6
	☽□☿	4 54
	☽□♂	9 35
	☽⊻♆	3pm 48
	☽⊻♅	8 38
	☽⊻♇	11 46
2 S	☽∠♃	0am 15
	☽△♀	4 27
	☉P♂	6 43
	☽⚹♄	4pm 52
	☉⚼♇	6 30
	☉⚻♃	11 18
3 SU	☽∠♇	2am 17
	☽⚹♃	2 37
	☽□☉	2 55
	☉⊥♄	2pm 33
	☽⚹☿	4 15
	☽⚹♂	5 57
	☽∠♄	8 10
	☽☌♆	9 15
4 M	☽☌♅	2am 26
	☿P♇	5 36
	☽⚹♇	5 36
	☉P☿	7 15
	☉P♇	9 40
	☽□♀	4pm 22
	☽P♃	6 32
	☿☌♂	8 43
	☽∠♂	11 34
	☽∠☿	11 45
5 TU	☽⊻♄	0am 15
	☽P♀	6 48
	☽□♃	9 41
	☿⚹♆	11 28
	☽⚹☉	3pm 7
	☽P♄	10 53
6 W	♂⚹♆	2am 5
	☽⊻♆	5 47
	☽⊻♂	6 1
	☽⊻☿	8 23
	☽⊻♅	11 16
	☽□♇	2pm 24
	☽P☉	7 12
	☽∠☉	10 31
7 TH	☽P♇	0am 32
	☿⚹♅	7 11
	☽⚹♀	8 10
	☽☌♄	10 30
	☽∠♆	11 0
	☽P☿	11 38

	☽P♂	2pm 22
	☽∠♅	4 37
	☽△♃	7 19
8 F	☿⚼♃	3am 18
	☿△♇	6 35
	☽⊻☉	6 37
	♀⚹♄	9 15
	☽⚹♆	4pm 42
	☽∠♀	5 10
	☿P♂	7 21
	☽☌♂	8 59
	☽⚹♅	10 25
	☽P☿	11 34
	☽P♂	11 54
9 S	♀P♃	0am 32
	☽⚼♃	0 52
	☽△♇	1 28
	☽☌☿	4 29
	☽P♇	4pm 24
	♂⚹♅	7 35
	☽⊻♄	10 45
10 SU	☽⊻♀	2am 43
	♄∠♆	4 14
	☽P☉	5 47
	☽⚼♇	7 35
	☽P♄	6pm 7
11 M	☽☌☉	0am 17
	♂⚼♃	1 50
	☽□♆	5 10
	☽∠♄	5 22
	☽□♅	11 2
	☽⊻♂	1pm 46
	♀☍♃	2 53
	♂△♇	4 22
	☉±♇	5 54
	☽P♃	11 44
12 TU	☽⊻☿	3am 12
	☽⚹♄	0pm 8
	☽P♀	0 26
	♀∠♂	4 44
	☽☍♃	7 7
	☿Q♆	7 29
	☽∠♂	10 27
	☽•♀	10 42
13 W	☿±♃	3am 44
	☉□♆	11 30
	☽∠☿	3pm 1
	☽△♆	6 14
	☽⊻☉	6 50
	☉∠♄	7 46
14 TH	☽△♅	0am 9
	☽☍♇	2 51
	☽⚹♂	7 5
	☿P♂	7 55
	☿Q♅	11 22
	☿⊻♄	6pm 12
15 F	☽⚼♆	0am 35
	☽□♄	1 30
	☽⚹☿	2 43
	☽∠☉	3 53
	☉P♄	5 40
	☽⚼♅	6 28
	☽⊻♀	6pm 18
16 S	☿⚻♃	7am 21
	☉□♅	11 41
	☽⚹☉	0pm 23
	☽⚼♃	0 50
	☿⊥♀	6 47
	☿⚼♇	7 55

	☽□♂	11 2
17 SU	☽∠♀	3am 11
	☽△♄	1pm 11
	☉⚻♇	5 41
	☽△♃	5 43
	☽⚼♇	7 51
18 M	☽□☿	0am 3
	♃Q♆	0 10
	☿⊥♄	5 3
	☽P♀	6 56
	☽⚹♀	11 0
	☽☍♆	4pm 23
	☽⚼♄	5 51
	☽☍♅	9 53
19 TU	☽△♇	0am 2
	♀Q♄	0 18
	☽□☉	2 34
	☽△♂	11 28
	☽P♃	4pm 19
	☿P♇	10 17
20 W	☽□♃	0am 53
	☽P☉	7 16
	☽⚼♂	3pm 56
	☽△☿	4 17
	☽P♄	6 28
	♀△♆	7 31
	☽□♀	10 47
21 TH	♂±♃	3am 15
	☽□♇	5 30
	☽P☿	9 2
	☽△☉	11 56
	☿±♇	0pm 2
	☽P♇	3 11
	♂Q♆	3 27
	☽⚼☿	10 13
22 F	☽⚼♆	0am 6
	☽☍♄	1 54
	☽⚹♃	4 15
	☽⚼♅	5 4
	☽P♂	10 56
	☿□♆	11 47
	☽⚼☉	2pm 54
23 S	☽△♆	0am 53
	☽P♂	1 7
	☿∠♄	1 45
	☽∠♃	4 42
	☽△♀	5 42
	☽△♅	5 43
	♀△♅	5 58
	☽⚹♇	7 23
	☽P♇	7pm 12
	☽☍♂	11 7
	☿□♅	11 21
24 SU	♀☍♇	1am 48
	☽⊻♃	4 36
	☽∠♇	7 23
	☽⚼♀	7 53
	☿P♄	11 3
	☿⚻♇	11 6
	☽P♄	1pm 46
	☽P☿	2 23
25 M	☽□♆	0am 50
	☿⊻♀	1 8
	☽⚼♄	2 56
	☽□♅	5 31
	☽⊻♇	7 3
	☽P☉	9 38
	☽☍☿	10 11
	♆Stat	10 51

	☽P♃	0pm 8
	♂Q♅	0 12
	☽☍☉	7 45
26 TU	☽△♄	2am 42
	☽☌♃	3 34
	☉P♃	2pm 55
	♀P♆	7 18
27 W	☽⚹♆	0am 11
	☽⚼♂	2 5
	☽⚹♅	4 57
	☽☌♇	6 24
	♂⊻♄	0pm 50
	☽☍♀	1 19
	♂⚻♃	7 38
28 TH	☽∠♆	0am 16
	☽□♄	2 51
	☽⊻♃	3 4
	☽△♂	3 32
	☽∠♅	5 8
	♀P♅	5pm 50
	♃△♄	5 56
	☽⚼☿	10 1
29 F	☽⊻♆	0am 55
	☽⚼☉	1 10
	☽∠♃	3 35
	☿P♃	4 19
	☽⊻♅	5 55
	☽⊻♇	7 21
30 S	☽△☿	3 55
	☽△☉	4 30
	☽⚹♃	4 50
	☽⚹♄	5 22
	☽□♂	8 46
	☉☍♃	8 55
	☽∠♇	8 56
	☿☍♃	9 39
	☉☌☿	10 21
	♂⚼♇	11 40
	☿⚹♄	1pm 40
	☉⚹♄	6 3
	☉P☿	8 55
	♅Stat	10 22
MAY		
1 SU	☽⚼♀	0am 1
	☽☌♆	4 36
	☽∠♄	7 56
	☽☌♅	9 59
	☽⚹♇	11 24
	☽P☿	3pm 37
	☽P☉	6 26
2 M	☿⊻♂	1am 48
	☽△♀	5 52
	☽P♃	7 14
	☽□♃	10 2
	☽⊻♄	11 27
	☽□☉	2pm 32
	☽⚹♂	6 11
	☽□☿	8 20
3 TU	♀⚼♆	2am 51
	☽P♄	9 37
	☽⊻♆	11 59
	☽⊻♅	5pm 44
	☽□♇	7 9
	♀⚻♃	10 35
4 W	☽∠♂	0am 33
	☽P♇	7 4
	☽P♂	9 7
	☽∠♆	4pm 58

	☽△♃	6 44
	☽□♀	9 11
	☽☌♄	9 11
	♀□♄	9 13
	☽∠♅	10 53
5 TH	☽⚹☉	5am 5
	☽⊻♂	7 50
	♂P♇	1pm 21
	♀⚼♅	2 12
	☽⚹☿	6 46
	☽⚹♆	10 38
6 F	☽⚼♃	0am 8
	☽⚹♅	4 40
	♂⊥♄	5 43
	☽△♇	6 1
	☿Q♄	8 16
	☿⊥♂	9 33
	☽∠☉	1pm 37
	☿△♆	4 30
	☽P♇	8 50
	☽P♂	11 23
7 S	☽∠☿	7am 28
	☽⊻♄	9 32
	☽⚼♇	0pm 12
	☽⚹♀	4 0
	☽P♄	6 44
	☽⊻☉	10 39
8 SU	☽☌♂	0am 17
	☿△♅	2 37
	☿☍♇	9 50
	♀±♃	10 11
	☽□♆	11 12
	☽∠♄	4pm 11
	☽□♅	5 20
	☿P♆	6 57
	☽⊻☿	8 31
	☽P♃	10 1
9 M	☽∠♀	1am 59
	☿P♅	5pm 17
	☽☍♃	6 20
	☽⚹♄	10 54
10 TU	☽⊻♀	11am 59
	♀±♆	0pm 14
	☽P☉	0 45
	☽•●	5 7
	☽⊻♂	5 31
11 W	☽△♆	0am 9
	☽△♅	6 15
	☽☍♇	7 25
	☉⊻♂	2pm 50
	♂±♇	8 25
	☽☌☿	9 58
12 TH	☽∠♂	1am 52
	☽⚼♆	6 22
	☽□♄	11 50
	☽⚼♅	0pm 24
	♀±♅	11 43
13 F	☽☌♀	7am 2
	☽⚹♂	9 47
	☽⊻☉	10 34
	☿∠♂	10 42
	☽⚼♃	11 57
	☿⚻♃	11pm 31
14 S	☿⚼♆	1am 43
	☉Q♄	3 15
	☉△♆	6 48
	☽△♃	5pm 2
	☽∠☉	6 27
	☽⊻☿	8 21

	☽△♄	11 10
	♂□♆	11 54
15 SU	☽⚼♇	0am 20
	☽P☉	2 56
	♀⚼♃	4 35
	♀⚻♆	10 37
	☿□♄	4pm 6
	☿⚼♅	4 43
	☽☍♆	10 15
	☽⚺♀	11 29
	☽□♂	11 41
16 M	☽⚹☉	1am 32
	☽⚼♄	3 54
	☽☍♅	3 56
	☽△♇	4 51
	♀⚹♂	5 3
	☽∠☿	5 46
	♄∠♅	7 38
17 TU	☽□♃	1 19
	☿±♃	2 9
	♂P♄	4 15
	☽P♃	5 28
	☽∠♀	6 18
	☉△♅	8 53
	☽⚹☿	1pm 50
	☿P♀	7 46
	☉☍♇	8 21
	♀⚻♅	10 3
18 W	☽P♂	3am 35
	☽P♄	5 13
	♀⚻♇	7 8
	☽△♂	10 9
	☽□♇	11 38
	☽⚹♀	0pm 5
	☽□☉	0 50
	♂□♅	9 51
	☽P♇	11 36
19 TH	☿±♆	3am 58
	♂∠♄	4 12
	☽⚹♃	6 35
	☽⚼♆	7 51
	♂⚻♇	11 43
	☽⚼♅	1pm 3
	☽☍♄	1 27
	☽⚼♂	1 56
20 F	☽□☿	1am 49
	☉⚺♀	3 47
	☽∠♃	8 5
	☽△♆	9 29
	☽△♅	2pm 32
	☽⚹♇	3 15
	☽△☉	8 12
	☽□♀	8 30
21 S	☿±♅	1am 27
	☽P♇	3 47
	☽⚺♃	8 54
	☽∠♇	4pm 2
	☽P♄	8 29
	☽⚼☉	10 39
22 SU	☽P♂	4am 1
	☿⚼♃	9 1
	☽△☿	9 11
	☽□♆	10 50
	☽□♅	3pm 40
	☽⚺♇	4 19
	☽⚼♄	4 23
	☽P♃	4 50
	☽☍♂	8 32
23	☽△♀	1am 43

M	☿⚻♆	2 16
	♀±♇	4 22
	☽☌♃	9 5
	☽⚼☿	11 46
	☽△♄	4pm 28
24 TU	☽⚼♀	3am 43
	☽⚹♆	10 45
	☽⚹♅	3pm 31
	☽☌♇	4 8
	☉P♆	9 8
25 W	☽☍☉	3am 39
	☿⚻♅	7 13
	☽⚺♃	8 37
	☽∠♆	10 42
	☿⚻♇	2pm 21
	☽∠♅	3 30
	☽□♄	4 32
26 TH	☽⚼♂	0am 18
	☽∠♃	8 41
	☽⚺♆	10 57
	♀△♃	3pm 24
	☽⚺♅	3 49
	☽⚺♇	4 26
	☽☍☿	6 52
27 F	☽△♂	2am 11
	☽⚹♃	9 16
	☽☍♀	11 1
	☽∠♇	5pm 20
	☽⚹♄	6 2
28 S	☉⚻♃	2am 18
	☉P♅	8 25
	☽⚼☉	11 12
	☽☌♆	1pm 13
	☽☌♅	6 22
	☽⚹♇	7 0
	☽∠♄	7 51
29 SU	☽□♂	8am 28
	☽□♃	0pm 40
	☽△☉	3 35
	☉⚼♆	3 56
	☽P♃	9 41
	☽P♂	10 17
	☽⚺♄	10 35
30 M	♂P♃	6am 13
	☽⚼☿	7 20
	♀⚼♇	1pm 6
	☽⚺♆	6 59
	☽P♄	8 15
	☿±♇	10 55
31 TU	☽⚺♅	0am 29
	☽□♇	1 9
	♀△♄	1 37
	☽⚼♀	2 25
	☽△☿	1pm 32
	☽P♇	2 59
	☽⚹♂	7 14
	☽△♃	7 51
	☽∠♆	11 20

JUNE

1 W	☽□☉	4am 2
	♂☍♃	4 36
	☽∠♅	5 1
	☽☌♄	7 4
	☽△♀	10 7
	☉⚼♅	4pm 24
2 TH	☽⚼♃	0am 50
	☽∠♂	2 18
	☽⚹♆	4 34

	☽⚹♅	10 24
	☽△♇	11 5
	☉±♃	7pm 37
	☉□♄	8 31
3 F	☽P♇	2am 39
	☽□☿	4 29
	☽⚺♂	10 14
	☽⚼♇	5pm 6
	☽⚺♄	6 51
	☽⚹☉	8 44
	☽P♄	10 25
4 S	☽□♀	4am 31
	☿△♃	1pm 38
	☽□♆	4 51
	☽P♃	10 26
	☽□♅	10 48
5 SU	☽∠♄	1am 24
	☽∠☉	5 55
	☽P♂	10 45
	☽☍♃	7pm 2
	☽⚹☿	8 43
6 M	☽☌♂	3am 15
	☿P♀	5 54
	☽⚹♄	8 0
	☽⚺☉	3pm 8
7 TU	☽⚹♀	0am 19
	☽∠☿	4 25
	☽△♆	5 44
	☽△♅	11 35
	☽☍♇	0pm 17
	☉±♆	9 5
8 W	☽∠♀	9am 48
	☽⚺☿	11 30
	☽⚼♆	11 47
	☽⚼♅	5pm 33
	☽⚺♂	7 39
	☽□♄	8 29
9 TH	☉⊥♂	0am 4
	♀☍♆	5 42
	☽☌☉	8 26
	♂⚹♄	9 44
	☽⚼♃	0pm 51
	☽⚺♀	6 39
10 F	☉P☿	0am 6
	☽∠♂	3 2
	☽△♃	5pm 54
	☉±♅	7 49
	☽☌☿	11 23
11 S	☉P♀	0am 53
	☽⚼♇	4 39
	☽△♄	7 2
	☽⚹♂	9 46
	☉⚼♃	1pm 28
	♀☍♅	3 6
	♀△♇	10 18
	☽⚺☉	11 11
12 SU	♀Q♂	2am 32
	☽☍♆	2 57
	☽☍♅	8 20
	☽△♇	9 1
	☽☌♀	10 8
	☽⚼♄	11 27
	☽P♂	3pm 17
	☿Stat	5 48
13 M	♀⚼♄	0am 40
	☽□♃	2 20
	☽∠☉	5 27
	☽⚺☿	8 3
	☽P♃	3pm 54

	☽□♂	9 8
14 TU	☉⚻♆	0am 22
	☽⚹☉	10 59
	☽∠☿	11 14
	☽P♄	0pm 49
	☽□♇	4 1
	☽⚺♀	10 29
15 W	☉⊥♀	5am 1
	☽P♇	6 12
	☿P♅	7 19
	☽⚹♃	8 31
	☽⚼♆	0pm 59
	☽⚹☿	1 42
	☽⚼♅	5 59
	☽☍♄	9 11
16 TH	☽∠♀	3am 32
	☽△♂	5 45
	☽∠♃	10 46
	☽△♆	3pm 11
	☽□☉	7 57
	☽△♅	8 4
	☽⚹♇	8 46
	☉⚻♅	9 43
17 F	☉⚻♇	7am 35
	♀P♅	7 41
	☽⚹♀	7 52
	☽⚼♂	9 5
	☽P♇	10 58
	☽⚺♃	0pm 30
	☿P♆	3 34
	☽□☿	4 39
	☽∠♇	10 20
18 S	☽P♄	3am 21
	☽□♆	6pm 5
	☽P♃	10 11
	☽□♅	10 45
	☽⚺♇	11 27
19 SU	☽⚼♄	2am 0
	☽△☉	2 21
	♀P♆	1pm 20
	♀□♃	1 52
	☽☌♃	2 36
	☽□♀	2 40
	☽△☿	5 26
20 M	☽△♄	2am 46
	☽⚼☉	4 49
	☽P♂	8 42
	☿⚺♀	3pm 54
	☽☍♂	4 0
	☽⚼☿	5 15
	♀±♄	6 31
	☽⚹♆	7 26
	☽⚹♅	11 59
21 TU	☽☌♇	0am 42
	☿∠♂	7 30
	☽P☿	1pm 36
	☽⚺♃	3 34
	☽P♀	6 44
	☽∠♆	7 51
	☽△♀	7 59
22 W	☽∠♅	0am 22
	☽□♄	3 45
	☽∠♃	4pm 1
	☽⚺♆	8 20
	☽⚼♀	10 37
23 TH	☽⚺♅	0am 52
	☽⚺♇	1 39
	♄Stat	3 59
	☿△♃	5 46

	☉±♇	11 7
	☽☍☉	11 33
	♂△♆	11 52
	☽☍☿	4pm 17
	☽⚹♃	4 41
	☽P♀	9 24
	☽⚼♂	9 34
	☽P☿	10 35
24 F	☽∠♇	2am 28
	☿⊥♀	3 59
	☽⚹♄	5 14
	☿P♀	9 46
	☽P♂	1pm 58
	☽☌♆	10 16
25 S	☽△♂	0am 11
	☽☌♅	2 56
	☽⚹♇	3 48
	☽∠♄	6 41
	☉☌☿	9 57
	☽□♃	7pm 33
	♀⚻♄	10 15
26 SU	♂Q♄	2am 23
	☽⚺♄	8 51
	☽☍♀	9 51
	☽P♃	10 13
	☉△♃	3pm 56
	☽⚼☿	6 34
	☽⚼☉	10 37
	♀P♂	10 54
27 M	☽⚺♆	2am 52
	♂△♅	3 25
	☽P♄	6 10
	☽⚺♅	7 48
	☽□♂	8 4
	☽□♇	8 48
	☽△☿	8pm 52
	♂☍♇	9 3
28 TU	☽P♇	0am 12
	☽△♃	1 39
	☽△☉	4 24
	☽∠♆	6 32
	☿⊥♂	7 29
	☽∠♅	11 38
	☽☌♄	3pm 57
	☿P♂	4 5
	☿±♇	10 47
29 W	☽⚼♃	6am 9
	☿∠♀	9 46
	☽⚹♆	11 10
	☽⚹♅	4pm 24
	☽△♇	5 33
	☽⚹♂	8 23
30 TH	☽□☿	4am 12
	☽⚼♀	6 56
	☽P♇	10 53
	☽□☉	7pm 31
	☽⚼♇	11 12

JULY

1 F	☽⚺♄	2am 41
	☽∠♂	4 3
	☽P♄	6 30
	☽△♀	4pm 9
	☽□♆	10 46
2 S	♃Stat	3am 35
	☽□♅	4 8
	☽P♃	4 40
	☽∠♄	8 58
	☽⚺♂	0pm 19

	☽✱☿	2 36
	☉⚼♇	5 12
3	☽☍♃	0am 5
SU	☽P♀	0pm 26
	☽✱☉	1 34
	☽✱♄	3 26
	☿⊻♂	4 9
	☽∠☿	8 25
4	♀⚻♆	11am 5
M	☽△♆	11 34
	☽□♀	11 37
	☉△♄	0pm 18
	☽P☿	4 31
	☽△♅	4 51
	☽☍♇	6 15
	♀Q♃	10 27
	☽∠☉	10 36
5	☽⊻☿	2am 17
TU	☽☌♂	5 1
	☽P♂	0pm 6
	☽⚼♆	5 37
	☽⚼♅	10 48
6	☽□♄	3am 39
W	☽⊻☉	7 5
	♀⚻♅	4pm 27
	☽⚼♃	6 29
	☿ Stat	7 42
7	☽✱♀	5am 23
TH	♀□♇	7 46
	☽☌☿	1pm 13
	☽P♂	2 22
	☽⊻♂	7 34
	☽△♃	11 32
8	☽⚼♇	10am 20
F	☽P☿	11 43
	☽∠♀	0pm 59
	☽△♄	1 35
	☽☌☉	9 37
9	☽∠♂	1am 39
S	☽☍♆	8 8
	☽☍♅	0pm 53
	♀±♆	2 22
	☽△♇	2 23
	☽⚼♄	5 31
	☽⊻♀	7 41
	☽⊻☿	10 24
10	☽✱♂	6am 57
SU	☽□♃	7 38
	☽P♀	3pm 48
	♂⚻♃	8 16
	☽P♃	10 34
11	☽∠☿	2am 22
M	☽⊻☉	8 55
	☿✱♀	3pm 2
	☽P♄	6 9
	♀±♅	6 49
	☽□♇	8 43
12	☽✱☿	6am 0
TU	☽☌♀	6 50
	☽P♇	0pm 5
	♂P♆	0 6
	☽✱♃	1 31
	☽∠☉	1 36
	☽□♂	3 40
	☽⚼♆	5 11
	☽⚼♅	9 37
	♀P♃	11 56
13	☽☍♄	2am 5
W	☽∠♃	3pm 51

	☿±♇	3 55
	☽✱☉	5 49
	☽△♆	7 22
	♂⚼♆	8 18
	☽△♅	11 42
14	☉P♅	0am 42
TH	☽✱♇	1 19
	☽□☿	0pm 38
	☉☍♆	3 32
	☽⊻♀	3 51
	☽P♇	5 42
	☽⊻♃	5 53
	☽△♂	10 36
15	☽∠♇	3am 9
F	☽P♄	11 16
	♀✱♃	5pm 51
	☽∠♀	7 48
	☉P♂	8 51
	☽P♀	10 7
	☽□♆	10 51
16	☽□☉	1am 12
S	☽⚼♂	1 35
	☽□♅	3 4
	☽⊻♇	4 45
	☽P♃	5 59
	☽⚼♄	7 26
	☽△☿	6pm 49
	☽☌♃	9 12
	☉∠♂	9 47
	☽✱♀	11 28
17	☉☍♅	3am 54
SU	♂⚼♅	6 3
	☽△♄	8 45
	♀⚼♆	9 19
	☽⚼☿	9pm 51
18	☽✱♆	1am 30
M	☉△♇	5 15
	☽✱♅	5 37
	☉P♆	6 48
	☽☌♇	7 23
	☽△☉	7 32
	☿△♃	9 11
	♂P♅	1pm 32
	☉P☿	2 59
	☿P♆	10 54
	☽⊻♃	11 52
19	☽∠♆	2am 38
TU	☽□♀	6 13
	☽∠♅	6 43
	☽☍♂	9 20
	☽⚼☉	10 30
	☽□♄	11 1
	♀⚼♅	0pm 27
	☉⚼♄	6 1
	♂±♃	11 11
20	♀P♄	0am 43
W	☽∠♃	1 6
	☽⊻♆	3 44
	☽⊻♅	7 48
	☽⊻♇	9 41
	♂□♄	6pm 14
21	☽✱♃	2am 27
TH	☽☍☿	7 44
	☽∠♇	10 59
	☽△♀	0pm 58
	☽✱♄	1 22
	♀☍♄	5 58
22	☽☌♆	6am 26
F	☽☌♅	10 33

	☽✱♇	0pm 35
	☽∠♄	2 57
	☽⚼♀	4 50
	☽⚼♂	5 26
	☿⚼♇	7 11
	☽☍☉	8 16
23	♀Q♇	4am 17
S	☽□♃	6 5
	♀□♂	11 41
	☽⊻♄	5pm 1
	☿△♄	6 11
	☽P♃	6 14
	☿P♅	7 30
	☽△♂	9 3
24	☽⊻♆	10am 54
SU	☽P♄	1pm 59
	☽⊻♅	3 9
	☽□♇	5 25
	☽⚼☿	11 2
25	☽P♀	4am 11
M	☽P♇	9 25
	☽△♃	0pm 11
	☽∠♆	2 12
	☽∠♅	6 34
	☽☌♄	11 17
26	☽△☿	6am 38
TU	☽□♂	6 53
	♂±♆	9 1
	☽☍♀	9 17
	☿⊻♂	10 1
	☽⚼☉	11 58
	☽⚼♃	4pm 30
	☽✱♆	6 23
	☽✱♅	10 52
27	☽△♇	1am 25
W	♀P♇	2 57
	☽P♀	7pm 9
	☽△☉	7 20
	☽P♇	9 5
28	☽⚼♇	6am 43
TH	☽⊻♄	8 56
	☿✱♀	0pm 4
	☉±♄	5 29
	☽P♄	6 38
	☽✱♂	8 44
29	☽□☿	2am 30
F	☉□♃	4 26
	☽□♆	5 13
	☽□♅	9 51
	☽∠♄	2pm 51
	♂±♅	3 7
	☽P♃	5 23
	☿☍♆	8 22
30	♀∠♃	2am 39
S	☽∠♂	4 49
	☽☍♃	10 16
	☿P♅	10 45
	☽⚼♀	10 58
	☽□☉	0pm 40
	♀△♆	4 28
	☽✱♄	9 8
31	☿☍♅	1am 40
SU	☽⊻♂	1pm 9
	☽△♆	5 54
	☽P☉	7 18
	☿△♇	8 19
	☽△♀	8 31
	☿⊥♂	10 2
	☽△♅	10 30

AUGUST

1	☽☍♇	1am 33
M	☽✱☿	2 34
	☿⚼♄	7 49
	♀△♅	5pm 40
2	☽⚼♆	0am 6
TU	☽⚼♅	4 36
	☽✱☉	6 39
	☽□♄	9 24
	☽∠☿	2pm 30
3	♀✱♇	3am 55
W	☿P♆	4 17
	☽☌♂	4 48
	☽⚼♃	5 24
	☽□♀	2pm 7
	☽∠☉	2 42
	☉⚻♄	3 33
	♂⚼♃	5 8
	♂⚻♆	9 29
4	☽⊻☿	1am 29
TH	☽△♃	10 35
	☽⚼♇	5pm 59
	☽△♄	7 20
	☽⊻☉	9 44
5	☽☍♆	2 44
F	☿±♄	4 40
	♇ Stat	5 3
	☽⊻♂	5 4
	☽☍♅	6 48
	☽P☉	7 30
	☽△♇	9 54
	☽⚼♄	11 5
6	☽✱♀	3am 43
S	☉∠♀	4 39
	☿□♃	11 41
	☽□♃	6pm 26
	☽☌☿	7 36
	☽∠♂	9 45
7	♂⚻♅	1am 18
SU	☽P♃	2 0
	☽☌☉	8 45
	☽∠♀	8 58
	☿∠♂	3pm 10
	☽P♄	10 28
8	☽✱♂	1am 39
M	☽□♇	3 29
	♀⊥♃	7 51
	☿⚻♄	0pm 21
	☽⊻♀	1 26
	☽P♇	6 27
	☽⚼♆	10 37
	☽✱♃	11 30
9	☽⚼♅	2am 21
TU	☽☍♄	6 12
	☽⊻☿	9 24
	♂⚻♇	3pm 39
	☽P♀	3 51
	☽⊻☉	4 44
10	☽△♆	0am 16
W	☽∠♃	1 24
	☽△♅	3 57
	☽P♀	5 33
	☽✱♇	7 5
	☽□♂	7 51
	☽∠☿	3pm 23
	☽∠☉	8 8
	☽☌♀	8 54
11	☽P♇	1am 23

TH	☽⊻♃	3 4
	☽∠♇	8 33
	☽✱☿	9pm 7
	☽P♄	9 16
	☽✱☉	11 23
12	☽□♆	3am 5
F	☽□♅	6 41
	☽⊻♇	9 57
	☽⚼♄	10 19
	☽△♂	1pm 12
	☽P♃	5 36
13	☉☌☿	0am 54
S	☽⊻♀	3 43
	☽P☉	5 0
	☽☌♃	6 17
	☽△♄	11 36
	☿⚻♆	2pm 14
	☽P☿	2 41
	☿∠♀	2 59
	☽⚼♂	3 52
14	☉⚻♆	4am 44
SU	☽✱♆	5 52
	☽□☉	5 57
	☽∠♀	7 11
	☽□☿	8 31
	☽✱♅	9 27
	☽☌♇	0pm 52
	☿⚻♅	3 3
	♀⊻♃	7 21
15	☽∠♆	7am 24
M	☽⊻♃	9 45
	☽✱♀	10 45
	☽∠♅	10 58
	☽□♄	2pm 26
	☿□♇	3 21
	☿Q♃	6 46
16	☉⚻♅	7am 45
TU	☽⊻♆	9 2
	☽∠♃	11 41
	☽⊻♅	0pm 37
	☽△☉	1 0
	☿±♆	1 30
	☽⊻♇	4 13
	☽△☿	8 19
17	☽☍♂	0am 33
W	♀⚻♄	10 43
	☽✱♃	1pm 47
	☉P☿	1 58
	☿±♅	2 39
	♀∠♇	2 42
	☽⚼☉	4 49
	☽✱♄	5 49
	☽∠♇	6 9
	☽□♀	6 25
	☿P♃	8 27
18	☽⚼☿	2am 32
TH	☉P♃	3 29
	☉□♇	0pm 7
	☽☌♆	0 55
	♀P♇	1 45
	☿✱♂	3 48
	☽☌♅	4 31
	☽∠♄	7 51
	♂±♇	7 57
	☽✱♇	8 20
19	☉Q♃	5am 20
F	☽□♃	6pm 53
	☽P♃	8 15
	☽⊻♄	10 15

Day	Aspect	Time
20 S	☽P☉	0am 44
	☽△♀	3 22
	☉±♆	7 15
	☽P☿	8 25
	☽⚼♂	11 33
	☽⚺♆	6pm 8
	☽P♄	6 31
	☽⚺♅	9 50
21 SU	☽□♇	1am 56
	☿⚼♆	4 50
	☽☍☉	6 47
	☽⚼♀	8 43
	☽P♀	9 41
	☽△♂	4pm 18
	☽P♇	5 3
	☽∠♆	9 33
22 M	☽☍☿	0am 23
	☽∠♅	1 19
	☽△♃	1 57
	☽☌♄	4 35
	☿⚼♅	6 46
	☉±♅	8 43
	☿⚹♃	0pm 3
	☿P♄	0 44
23 TU	☽⚹♆	1am 39
	♀±♄	2 5
	☿☍♄	4 55
	☽⚹♅	5 30
	☽⚼♃	6 31
	☿⊥♀	8 25
	☽△♇	10 0
24 W	☽□♂	4 12
	☿P♀	7 8
	☽P♇	7 54
	☽⚺♄	1pm 39
	☽⚼♇	3 8
	☽P☿	9 9
25 TH	☽P♀	2am 12
	☽⚼☉	3 40
	☿Q♇	5 43
	☽☍♀	5 50
	☽P♄	8 54
	☽□♆	0pm 4
	☽P☉	2 47
	☽□♅	4 3
	☽∠♄	7 14
26 F	♃Q♆	2am 38
	☽⚼☿	6 40
	☽P♃	11 12
	☽△☉	0pm 21
	☽⚹♂	7 19
	♀⊥♇	9 43
27 S	☽☍♃	0am 34
	☽⚹♄	1 19
	♀P♄	0pm 16
	☉P♀	5 27
	☿P♇	5 41
	☽△☿	6 18
	☉P♄	11 15
28 SU	☽△♆	0am 38
	☽∠♂	3 33
	☽△♅	4 38
	☽☍♇	9 49
	♀□♆	11 48
	♃△♄	5pm 10
	☿Q♂	11 22
29 M	☽□☉	6am 41
	☽⚼♆	7 2
	☽⚼♀	8 42

Day	Aspect	Time
	☽⚼♅	10 59
	☉⚼♆	10 59
	☽⚺♂	11 41
	☽□♄	1pm 49
	☿△♆	1 50
30 TU	♀□♅	1 24
	☽□☿	4 46
	☽△♀	5 11
	☿△♅	5 36
	☽⚼♃	8 29
	☿⚺♀	10 59
	♂△♄	11 43
31 W	☉⚼♅	10am 23
	♀⚼♄	10pm 28
	☿∠♃	10 40
	☽⚹☉	11 3

SEPTEMBER

Day	Aspect	Time
1 TH	☽△♄	0am 30
	♂△♃	1 10
	☽△♃	1 57
	☽☌♂	1 59
	☽⚼♇	3 12
	☿⚹♇	8 43
	☉☍♄	4pm 40
	☽☍♆	10 42
2 F	☽☍♅	2am 17
	♂⚼♇	2 54
	☽⚼♄	4 33
	☽∠☉	5 35
	☽□♀	6 59
	☽△♇	7 21
	☽⚹☿	10 31
	♀⚺♇	0pm 29
	☉⚹♃	7 12
3 S	☽P♃	2am 27
	☽P♀	9 28
	☽□♃	9 57
	☽⚺☉	10 55
	☽⚺♂	0pm 3
	☽∠☿	5 9
4 SU	☽P♄	2am 49
	☽□♇	0pm 52
	☽∠♂	3 32
	☽⚹♀	4 5
	☽P☉	7 31
	☽⚺☿	10 30
5 M	☽P♇	1am 48
	☉⚹♂	5 41
	☽⚼♆	6 24
	☽⚼♅	9 38
	☽☍♄	11 24
	☽⚹♃	2pm 26
	☽⚹♂	6 13
	☽☌☉	6 33
	☽∠♀	7 14
6 TU	☽P☿	0am 41
	♀P♃	5 28
	☽△♆	7 36
	☉Q♇	9 16
	♃Q♅	10 6
	☽△♅	10 45
	☽P☿	2pm 31
	☽⚹♇	3 35
	☽∠♃	3 48
	☽⚺♀	9 49
7 W	☽☌☿	6am 44
	☿⊥♃	8 17
	☽P♇	11 3

Day	Aspect	Time
	☽P☉	11 57
	☽∠♇	4pm 25
	☽⚺♃	4 53
	☽□♂	10 15
	☉P♇	11 6
	☽⚺☉	11 54
8 TH	☽□♆	9am 8
	☽P♄	9 30
	☽□♅	0pm 15
	☽⚼♄	1 41
	☽⚺♇	5 10
	☉∠♀	7 28
9 F	☽☌♀	2am 19
	☽∠☉	2 24
	☽P♃	9 40
	☽⚺☿	1pm 49
	☽△♄	2 21
	☽P♀	6 25
	☿▽♄	6 47
	☽☌♃	6 59
10 S	☽△♂	2am 3
	☽⚹☉	5 5
	☽⚹♆	10 49
	☽⚹♅	1pm 57
	☽∠☿	5 37
	☽☌♇	7 5
	☉P☿	11 51
11 SU	☽⚼♂	4am 19
	☽⚺♀	7 23
	☿∠♇	8 35
	☽∠♆	0pm 3
	☽∠♅	3 12
	☽□♄	4 23
	☽⚹☿	9 47
	☽⚺♃	10 2
12 M	☿⚺♃	0am 32
	☽∠♀	10 27
	☽□☉	11 34
	☽⚺♆	1pm 38
	☽⚺♅	4 50
	☿P♇	6 41
	☽⚺♇	10 15
13 TU	☽∠♃	0am 7
	☽⚹♀	1pm 57
	☉△♆	4 54
	☽⚹♄	7 52
	☿±♄	8 9
14 W	☽∠♇	0am 27
	☽⚹♃	2 37
	☽□☿	7 33
	☽☍♂	1pm 39
	☽P♀	4 40
	☽☌♆	6 2
	☽△☉	8 0
	☽☌♅	9 19
	☽∠♄	10 13
15 TH	☽⚹♇	3am 4
	☉△♅	1pm 59
	☽P♃	4 6
	☽□♀	10 23
16 F	☽⚺♄	1am 1
	☽⚼☉	1 2
	☽□♃	9 1
	☽△☿	7pm 25
	☽P♄	8 4
17 S	☽⚺♆	0am 12
	☽⚺♅	3 35
	☽P☿	6 4
	☽□♇	9 41

Day	Aspect	Time
	♀△♄	7pm 2
	☽P♇	10 12
18 SU	☽⚼☿	2am 14
	☽⚼♂	3 31
	☽∠♆	4 2
	☿⊥♇	4 43
	☽∠♅	7 29
	☽☌♄	8 3
	☽△♀	8 53
	♂☍♆	2pm 21
	☽△♃	5 28
	☿□♆	8 36
	☽P☉	10 15
	♀Q♆	11 21
	☉⚹♇	11 39
19 M	☿□♂	2am 36
	☽⚹♆	8 26
	☽△♂	9 21
	☽⚹♅	11 56
	☽⚼♀	3pm 2
	☽P☉	3 25
	☽△♇	6 27
	☽☍☉	8 1
	☽⚼♃	10 35
20 TU	☿P♄	5am 11
	☿□♅	8 29
	☿⚼♄	0pm 1
	☽⚺♄	5 19
	☽P♇	5 56
	☽⚼♇	11 43
21 W	☉∠♃	11am 47
	♂☍♅	2pm 55
	♀Q♅	5 32
	♂⚼♄	6 53
	☽□♆	6 59
	☽P♄	10 28
	☽□♅	10 38
	☽∠♄	10 48
	☽□♂	11 2
22 TH	☽☍☿	2am 46
	☽P☿	5 50
23 F	☽⚹♄	4 48
	☽P♃	8 13
	☿⚺♇	9 17
	♄∠♅	10 52
	☽☍♀	1pm 7
	☽☍♃	5 27
	☽⚼☉	9 23
24 S	☽△♆	7am 31
	☽△♅	11 13
	♂P♅	0pm 25
	☽⚹♂	2 53
	☽☍♇	6 28
25 SU	☽△☉	6am 42
	☽⚼♆	2pm 4
	☽□♄	5 29
	☽⚼♅	5 45
	☽∠♂	11 1
26 M	☽⚼☿	7am 4
	♀P♆	8pm 57
27 TU	☽⚺♂	6am 46
	☽⚼♀	0pm 41
	☽⚼♃	2 2
	☽△☿	3 43
	♂△♇	6 22
28 W	☽□☉	0am 23
	☽△♄	5 12
	☽⚼♇	0pm 55
	♀P♂	3 7

Day	Aspect	Time
	☽△♀	7 16
	☽△♃	7 51
29 TH	☽☍♆	7am 12
	☽⚼♄	9 58
	☽☍♅	10 38
	☽△♇	5pm 38
	☽☌♂	7 46
	♀☌♃	9 51
	☽P♃	11 9
30 F	☽P☿	1am 15
	♀P♅	5 2
	☽□☿	5 31
	☉▽♄	9 5
	☽⚹☉	2pm 10
	☿P♃	11 8

OCTOBER

Day	Aspect	Time
1 S	☽□♃	4am 29
	☽□♀	5 2
	☽P♄	7 45
	☽∠☉	7pm 7
2 SU	☽□♇	0am 1
	♅Stat	1 48
	☽⚺♂	4 13
	☽P♇	9 43
	☽⚹☿	1pm 48
	☽⚼♆	4 13
	♆Stat	5 49
	☽☍♄	6 22
	☽⚼♅	7 19
	☉⊥♃	9 9
	☽P☉	10 10
	☽⚺☉	10 54
3 M	♂P♆	3am 57
	☽∠♂	6 50
	☽⚹♃	9 2
	☽⚹♀	10 13
	☽∠☿	4pm 10
	☽△♆	5 25
	☉⊥♀	8 13
	☽△♅	8 26
4 TU	☽⚹♇	2am 45
	☽⚹♂	8 40
	☽∠♃	10 9
	☽∠♀	11 32
	☽P☉	1pm 48
	☉∠♇	5 14
	☽⚺☿	5 40
	☽P♇	10 42
5 W	☽∠♇	3am 14
	☽☌☉	3 55
	☽⚺♃	10 48
	☽⚺♀	0pm 19
	☽□♆	6 14
	☽⚼♄	7 59
	♂±♄	8 5
	☽□♅	9 9
	☽P♄	10 52
6 TH	☉±♄	3am 18
	☽⚺♇	3 25
	☽□♂	10 59
	☉Q♂	1pm 45
	☽☌☿	7 12
	☽△♄	7 58
7 F	☽P♃	6am 8
	☽⚺☉	7 33
	☽•♃	11 39
	☽☌♀	1pm 20
	☽P☿	2 14

	☽✶♆	6 29
	☽✶♅	9 26
8 S	☽☌♇	3am 51
	☽∠☉	9 35
	☽△♂	1pm 21
	☽∠♆	6 55
	☽⚺☿	8 23
	☽□♄	8 26
	☽∠♅	9 55
9 SU	☿ Stat	6am 43
	☿△♄	8 31
	☉P♇	11 32
	☽✶☉	0pm 6
	☽⚺♃	1 27
	☽⚺♀	3 5
	☽⚼♂	3 7
	☽⚺♆	7 49
	☽∠☿	9 17
	☽⚺♅	10 54
10 M	☿△♄	0am 11
	☽⚺♇	5 39
	☉⚺♃	0pm 27
	☽∠♃	3 8
	☽∠♀	4 39
	☽✶☿	10 32
	☽✶♄	10 42
11 TU	☽∠♇	7am 26
	☉⚺♀	0pm 10
	☽✶♃	5 30
	☽✶♀	6 48
	☽□☉	7 17
	☽☌♆	11 26
12 W	☽∠♄	0am 46
	☽☌♅	2 40
	☽P☿	4 26
	☽P♃	7 53
	☽✶♇	9 53
13 TH	☽☍♂	0 30
	☽□☿	2 9
	☽⚺♄	3 31
	♀ Stat	5 41
	☿P♃	9 54
	☿□♂	9pm 7
	☽P♄	9 12
14 F	☽□♃	0am 22
	☽□♀	0 55
	☉⊥♇	3 14
	☉□♆	4 39
	☽⚺♆	5 46
	☽△☉	5 51
	☽⚺♅	9 11
	☽P☉	2pm 36
	☽□♇	4 52
	☉⚼♄	7 42
15 S	☽P♇	1am 29
	♀☌♃	4 13
	☽△☿	7 2
	☽∠♆	9 55
	☽☌♄	11 2
	☽⚼☉	0pm 24
	☽∠♅	1 26
	♂⚻♄	9 25
16 SU	☉□♅	1am 44
	☽△♀	9 15
	☽⚼☿	9 50
	☽△♃	9 59
	☽✶♆	2pm 41
	☽⚼♂	4 36
	☽✶♅	6 17

17 M	☽△♇	2am 24
	☽⚼♀	2pm 6
	☽⚼♃	3 43
	☽⚺♄	8 56
	☽△♂	11 16
18 TU	☽P♇	2am 32
	☽⚼♇	7 59
19 W	☽P☉	0 11
	☽□♆	1 48
	☽∠♄	2 38
	☽□♅	5 32
	☽P♄	8 53
	☽☍☉	0pm 18
	☽☍☿	7 15
	☽P☿	8 48
20 TH	☽✶♄	8am 44
	☉⚺♇	9 41
	☽□♂	2pm 5
21 F	☉☌☿	5am 17
	☽☍♀	6 25
	☽P♃	7 16
	☽☍♃	11 36
	☽△♆	2pm 28
	☽△♅	6 17
	☿⚺♇	8 2
22 S	☿P♄	0am 40
	☽☍♇	3 0
	☉P☿	5 40
	☽P♂	3pm 31
	☉P♄	4 53
	☽⚼♆	9 3
	☽□♄	9 34
23 SU	☽⚼♅	0am 53
	☽✶♂	5 55
	☽⚼☿	6 6
	☽⚼☉	4pm 1
24 M	☽△☿	9am 58
	☽∠♂	1pm 40
	☽⚼♀	10 50
25 TU	☽△☉	1am 2
	☿Q♂	6 22
	☽⚼♃	8 26
	☽△♄	9 59
	☽P♂	5pm 33
	☿□♅	7 0
	☽⚺♂	8 54
	☽⚼♇	10 4
26 W	☽△♀	3am 30
	☽△♃	2pm 30
	☽☍♆	3 14
	☽P♃	3 15
	☽⚼♄	3 27
	☽□☿	5 34
	☽☍♅	6 57
27 TH	☽△♇	3am 22
	☽□☉	4pm 44
28 F	☽P☉	1am 35
	♀P♅	2 18
	☽☌♂	8 50
	☽□♀	10 31
	♃✶♆	10 51
	☿⊥♇	0pm 54
	☽P♄	1 45
	☽□♃	11 58
29 S	☽✶☿	0am 5
	☿⚺♃	3 51
	♀□♂	6 36
	☉△♄	10 46
	☽□♇	11 12

	☽P☿	3pm 19
	☽P♇	5 13
	♄∠♆	6 4
30 SU	☽☍♄	2am 32
	☽⚼♆	2 33
	☽∠☿	2 36
	☽✶☉	3 47
	☿ Stat	4 5
	☽⚼♅	5 57
	♀P♆	1pm 11
	☽✶♀	1 56
	☽⚺♂	4 24
31 M	☽△♆	4am 22
	☽⚺☿	4 34
	☽✶♃	5 19
	☽∠☉	7 29
	☽△♅	7 40
	☽∠♀	2pm 20
	☽✶♇	3 5
	☽∠♂	6 36

NOVEMBER

1 TU	☿⊥♇	6am 5
	☽∠♃	6 38
	☽⚺☉	10 10
	☽P♇	11 14
	☽P☿	11 20
	☉Q♆	11 39
	☽⚺♀	2pm 3
	☽∠♇	3 49
	☽✶♂	8 0
2 W	♀Q♅	3am 40
	☽⚼♄	5 31
	☽□♆	5 42
	☽☌☿	7 4
	☽⚺♃	7 16
	☽□♅	8 51
	☽P♄	11 32
	☿⚺♃	3pm 48
	☽⚺♇	3 58
	☉☌♀	11 12
3 TH	☽△♄	5am 23
	☽P☉	10 59
	☉Q♅	11 53
	☽☌♀	0pm 8
	☽ • ●	1 36
	☽□♂	9 18
4 F	☿□♅	1am 1
	☽✶♆	5 19
	☽P♃	6 30
	☽P♂	7 9
	☽ • ♃	7 31
	☽✶♅	8 28
	☽⚺☿	8 52
	☽☌♇	3pm 33
	♂P♃	4 19
5 S	☽P♀	1am 30
	☽□♄	4 48
	☽∠♆	5 6
	♀Q♆	7 24
	☽∠♅	8 17
	☽⚺♀	9 48
	☽∠☿	10 9
	☽⚺☉	4pm 31
	☽△♂	10 29
6 SU	☽⚺♆	5am 12
	☽⚺♃	8 6
	☽⚺♅	8 27
	☽∠♀	9 0

	☽✶☿	0pm 3
	☽⚺♇	3 48
	☽∠☉	6 35
	☽⚼♂	11 41
7 M	☽✶♄	5am 25
	☽✶♀	8 44
	☽∠♃	9 9
	♃✶♅	11 9
	☽∠♇	4pm 44
	☽P♀	8 48
	☽✶☉	9 26
	☽P♃	11 41
8 TU	☽P♂	5am 41
	☽∠♄	6 41
	☽☌♆	7 8
	☽☌♅	10 37
	♀P♃	10 47
	☽✶♃	10 57
	☽P☉	11 4
	☿⚺♇	1pm 50
	☽✶♇	6 27
	☽□☿	6 53
9 W	♄ Stat	8am 35
	☽⚺♄	8 48
	☽□♀	10 19
	☉P♂	8pm 52
10 TH	☽P♄	1am 50
	☉P♀	4 56
	☽□☉	6 14
	☽☍♂	8 16
	☽⚺♆	0pm 23
	☽P☿	0 43
	♀P♂	3 53
	☽⚺♅	4 10
	☽□♃	5 18
11 F	☽□♇	0am 35
	♀△♄	2 51
	☽P♇	5 8
	☽△☿	6 59
	☿Q♂	10 16
	☽△♀	3pm 17
	☽☌♄	3 45
	☽∠♆	4 23
	☽∠♅	8 18
12 S	☉□♂	3am 56
	☽⚼☿	3pm 7
	☽⚼♀	7 1
	☽△☉	7 33
	☽✶♆	9 12
13 SU	☽✶♅	1am 16
	☽△♃	3 21
	☽△♇	10 11
	☉✶♆	4pm 13
	☿☌♀	6 1
	☿P♄	6 48
	☉P♃	11 47
14 M	☽⚼♂	1am 18
	☽⚺♄	1 59
	☽⚼☉	3 39
	☽⚼♃	9 30
	☽P♇	10 12
	☿△♄	1pm 27
	☽⚼♇	4 0
15 TU	☽∠♄	7am 59
	☽△♂	8 21
	☽□♆	8 46
	☽□♅	1pm 1
	☽P♄	3 23
	☉✶♅	7 52

	♂⚻♆	8 32
16 W	☽P☿	0am 33
	☽☍♀	9 59
	☽✶♄	2pm 20
	☽P♀	5 32
	♀Q♂	6 6
	☿Q♆	8 13
	☽☍☿	9 24
17 TH	☽P♂	7am 27
	☉☌♃	7pm 48
	☽△♆	9 42
	☽□♂	11 22
18 F	☽△♅	2am 4
	☽☍♃	6 12
	☿Q♅	6 26
	☽☍☉	6 57
	☽P♃	8 45
	☽☍♇	11 23
	☿P♀	4pm 46
19 S	☽P☉	2am 54
	☽□♄	3 24
	☽⚼♆	4 16
	☽⚼♅	8 40
20 SU	☽⚼♀	3 40
	☉☌♇	0pm 51
	☽✶♂	2 20
21 M	☽P☉	0am 3
	☽⚼☿	6 17
	☽△♀	9 32
	☽△♄	3pm 58
	♂⚻♅	4 29
	☿P♂	5 46
	☽∠♂	9 22
22 TU	☽⚼♃	2am 39
	☽P♃	3 16
	☽⚼♇	6 20
	☽⚼☉	9 57
	☽△☿	4pm 30
	☽⚼♄	9 42
	☽☍♆	10 34
23 W	☽☍♅	2am 55
	☽P☿	3 47
	☽⚺♂	3 54
	☽△♃	8 41
	☽△♇	11 51
	☽P♂	0pm 34
	♀ Stat	4 56
	☽△☉	5 54
	☽□♀	8 21
24 TH	☽P♀	11am 36
	☿✶♆	4pm 25
	☽P♄	9 33
25 F	☉⚺♀	0am 50
	☽□☿	10 18
	☽☌♂	2pm 47
	☽□♃	6 37
	☽□♇	8 48
	☽P♇	11 36
26 S	☿✶♅	3am 30
	☽✶♀	4 54
	☽□☉	7 4
	☽☍♄	10 57
	☽⚼♆	11 45
	☽⚼♅	3pm 51
27 SU	☽∠♀	8am 3
	☿□♂	8 31
	☽△♆	2pm 29
	☉P♆	6 3
	☽△♅	6 29

	☿ P ♃	7	42		☽ ☌ ☉	11	54	S	☿ ∠ ♀	5	47		☉ ⚹ ♃	10	20
	☽ ⚹ ♂	10	0	3	☿ P ♅	1am	48	18	☽ ∠ ♅	5	25		☽ ⚹ ♇	2	17
	☽ ⚹ ☿	11	21	S	☽ ∠ ♀	1pm	45	SU	☽ ⚹ ♀	5	25		☽ ⚹ ♂	11	13
28	☽ ⚹ ♃	1am	4		♂ ± ♆	2	23		☽ ⚹ ☿	7	23		☽ ∠ ♀	4pm	26
M	☽ ⚹ ♇	2	24		☽ ⚹ ♆	5	19	10	☽ P ♃	8	27		☽ ⚹ ♃	6	27
	☽ ⚹ ♀	10	22		☽ ⚹ ♅	9	6	S	☽ ⚹ ♇	0pm	54		☽ ⚹ ♃	6	35
	☉ □ ♄	11	25	4	☽ △ ♂	3am	7		☽ □ ♀	6	21		☽ □ ☉	7	6
	☽ ⚹ ☉	3pm	55	SU	☿ □ ♄	3	32		♀ Q ♃	1	4	26	☽ □ ☿	8am	17
	☿ ☌ ♃	4	40		☽ ⚹ ♇	4	20	19	☿ ⚹ ♇	4	13	M	☽ P ♇	8	17
	☉ ∠ ♆	10	8		☽ ⚹ ♃	4	53	M	☽ △ ♄	0am	20		☽ ∠ ♇	1pm	34
	☽ P ♇	10	55		☿ ∠ ♅	9	39		♀ Q ♂	11	41		☽ ∠ ♂	6	45
29	☽ ∠ ♂	0am	13		☽ ⚹ ♀	2pm	17	11	☽ ⚹ ♄	9am	57		☽ ∠ ♃	9	3
TU	☿ ☌ ♇	2	53		☽ ⚹ ♄	4	43	SU	☽ P ♇	6pm	14		☽ ⚹ ♀	10	13
	☽ ∠ ♃	2	57		☽ P ♃	4	54		☿ ⊥ ♅	9	29	27	☽ P h	3am	8
	☽ ∠ ♇	3	55		☿ P ♅	5	35	12	☽ ⚹ ♇	0am	20	TU	☽ □ ♆	3	23
	☽ ∠ ♀	4	2		☽ ⚹ ☿	6	14	M	☽ □ ♂	2	32		☽ □ ♄	3	45
	☽ □ ♄	4pm	43	5	☽ ⚹ ☉	3am	17		☽ □ ♃	3	53		☽ □ ♅	8	11
	☽ □ ♆	5	26	M	☽ □ ♂	3	47		☽ △ ☿	11	17		☉ ⊥ ♇	8	51
	☽ ∠ ♅	6	50		☽ ∠ ♇	4	35		☽ △ ☉	1pm	19		☽ ⚹ ♇	3pm	14
	☽ □ ♅	9	15		☽ ∠ ♃	5	27		☽ ∠ ♄	4	1		☽ ⚹ ♂	8	23
30	☽ P h	9	28		☽ ∠ ♄	5pm	17	21	☽ ⚹ ♂	0am	24		☽ ⚹ ♃	10	51
W	☽ ⚹ ♂	1am	36		☽ ☌ ♆	5	55	W	☽ △ ♃	2	0	28	☽ P ♂	11	71
	☽ P ♀	1	52		☽ ∠ ☿	9	46		☉ ⚹ ♅	6	29	W	☽ P ♀	4	22
	☽ ⚹ ♃	4	3		☽ ☌ ♅	9	56		h ∠ ♅	8	42		☽ △ h	5	9
	☽ ⚹ ♇	4	41		☿ ∠ ♅	11	21	13	☽ P ♃	9	34		☿ ∠ ♇	6	31
	☽ ⚹ ☿	7	41	6	☽ ⚹ ♇	5am	29	TU	☽ P ♀	1pm	25		☽ ⚹ ☿	5pm	30
	☽ ☌ ♀	0pm	51	TU	☽ ☌ ♀	5	58		☽ P ♇	6pm	59	22	☽ □ ♃	1am	50
	☽ △ h	5	10		☽ ⚹ ♃	6	42					TH	☽ □ ♃	2	40
	☽ P ♂	8	48		☽ P ♂	1pm	36		☽ P ♀	10	17	29	☽ P h	7	42
	☽ ⚹ ☉	8	57		☽ □ ♀	5	25		☽ □ ♇	10	32	TH	☽ ∠ ☉	5	9
					☽ ⚹ ♄	6	37		☽ ⚹ h	10	33		☽ ⚹ ♆	5	31
	DECEMBER				☉ P ☿	8	12	14	☉ ☌ ♂	3am	16		☽ ⚹ ♅	10	10
					☽ ⚹ h	6	37	W	☿ ⚹ ♆	3	46		☽ ☌ ♇	4pm	52
1	☉ ∠ ♅	7am	11	7	☽ ⚹ ♇	2am	24		☉ ⚹ ♆	4	3	23	☉ ⚹ h	6	17
TH	☉ P ♅	1pm	55	W	♂ □ ♇	3	21	F	☽ ☌ ♇	4	45		☽ ∠ ♀	8	59
	☽ ⚹ ♆	5	50		☽ P ♀	7	50		♀ Q ♆	11	50		☽ □ ♂	9	55
	☽ ⚹ ♅	9	33		☽ ⚹ ☉	9	44	15	♂ ± ♅	7pm	53	30	☽ • ♃	0am	46
2	☽ □ ♂	2am	40		☽ P h	0pm	21	TH	☽ △ ♅	5am	39	F	☽ ⚹ ♇	5	50
F	☽ • ♃	4	43		☽ ⚹ ♆	9	30		☽ △ h	10	55		☽ ∠ ♃	5	52
	☽ ☌ ♇	4	44		☿ ⊥ ♀	11	25		☽ ☌ ♇	7pm	53		☽ □ h	6	26
	♃ ☌ ♇	7	24	8	☉ ⊥ ♆	1am	37		☿ ⚹ ♅	9	33		☽ ⚹ ☉	7	15
	☉ ⊥ ♅	8	19	TH	☽ ⚹ ♅	8	23		☽ □ ♂	11	33		☽ ∠ ♅	10	30
	☽ P ♃	10	56		♀ △ h	8	23	16	☿ ☌ ♀	11	57		♀ ⚹ ♅	0pm	22
	☽ ☌ ☿	1pm	2		☽ □ ♇	10	0	F	☽ ☌ ♃	0am	53	31	☽ ⚹ ♇	0am	2
	☽ ⚹ ♀	1	31		☽ ☌ ♂	10	33		☽ □ h	11	55	S	☽ ⚹ ♆	6	0
	☽ □ ♄	4	55		☽ P ♃	11	35		☽ □ ♅	5	31		☽ ⚹ ♀	7	5
	☽ ∠ ♆	5	34		☽ □ ♃	0pm	2		☽ P ♃	6	16		☽ ⚹ ♅	10	39
	☿ ⚹ ♀	6	41	9	☽ ☌ h	0am	13	25	☉ ⚹ ♅	7	45		☿ ∠ ♃	0pm	12
	☽ ∠ ♅	9	18	F	☽ △ ♀	0	48	SU	☉ Q ♃	2am	5		☽ ⚹ ♇	5	11
													☽ △ ♂	10	12

NOTE. — To obtain Local Mean Time of aspect, *add* the time equivalent of the Longitude if *East* and *subtract* if *West*.

G.M.T. AND EPHEMERIS TIME

The tabulations and times in this Ephemeris are in G.M.T.

From 1960 to 1982 the tabulations were in Ephemeris Time (E.T.), but it should be pointed out that the maximum correction to phenomena or aspects using E.T. as compared with G.M.T. did not exceed 53 seconds and that any correction should be considered as negligible in normal use.

DISTANCES APART OF ALL ☌s AND ☍s IN 1994

Note: The Distances Apart are in Declination

JANUARY

Day	Aspect	Time	°	′
1	☿ σ ♂	11am37	0	50
1	D o° h	3pm11	6	11
3	⊙ σ ☿	8pm20	1	48
6	♀ σ ♂	5am 1	0	18
6	D σ ♃	8pm32	2	54
8	D σ ♇	0am56	13	54
8	☿ σ Ψ	10am49	2	36
9	⊙ σ ♅	6am 7	1	34
11	⊙ σ Ψ	7am33	0	36
11	D σ ♂	3pm32	4	30
11	D σ ♀	8pm46	4	32
11	D σ Ψ	10pm 2	3	13
12	D σ ⊙	11pm10	3	51
12	D σ ♅	0am27	4	20
12	D σ ♀	9am31	6	12
12	♀ σ Ψ	10am40	1	23
12	⊙ σ ♅	4pm59	0	27
13	♀ σ ♅	1pm56	0	22
14	D σ h	7pm 2	6	7
16	♂ σ Ψ	2pm53	1	31
17	⊙ σ ♀	2am 4	0	55
18	♂ σ ♅	3pm43	0	29
20	D o° ♃	10pm30	2	42
22	D o° ♇	4am56	13	51
22	D o° Ψ	9am36	3	15
26	D o° ♅	0pm33	4	23
26	D o° ⊙	11pm 0	5	10
27	D o° ♀	1pm33	4	29
27	D o° ⊙	6pm 6	5	43
28	D o° ♀	6pm42	5	40
29	D o° h	3am41	6	3

FEBRUARY

Day	Aspect	Time	°	′
1	☿ σ h	6pm26	1	6
3	D σ ♃	7am 6	2	31
4	D σ ♇	7am34	13	48
8	D σ Ψ	7am26	3	19
8	D σ ♅	10am58	4	28
9	D σ ♂	4pm18	5	33
10	D σ ⊙	2pm30	4	42
11	D σ ♀	2am52	6	2
11	D σ h	9am25	6	0
11	D σ ☿	8pm52	2	23
14	♀ σ h	2am52	0	1
16	☿ σ ♀	4pm44	4	32
17	D o° ♃	10am45	2	22
18	D o° ♇	2pm10	13	44
19	☿ σ ♅	8am 3	4	46
20	⊙ σ ☿	8am 1	3	29
21	D o° h	5am 3	1	20
22	D o° Ψ	9pm20	3	26
23	D o° ♅	1am17	4	35
24	D o° ⊙	11pm50	5	46
25	D o° ♂	7am14	1	33
25	D o° h	6pm56	5	59
26	D o° ♀	1am15	4	36
26	D o° ♀	6pm19	5	38
28	☿ σ ♂	0am59	3	46

MARCH

Day	Aspect	Time	°	′
2	D σ ♃	2pm57	2	17
3	D σ ♇	1pm36	13	42
7	D σ Ψ	2pm43	3	32
7	D σ ♅	7pm15	4	42
10	D σ ☿	1am10	4	9
10	D σ ♂	6pm10	5	43
10	D σ h	10pm41	5	59
12	D σ ⊙	7am 5	4	11
13	D σ ♀	0pm10	4	37
14	⊙ σ h	5am 1	0	19
16	D o° ♃	5pm29	2	14
17	D o° ♇	9pm25	13	40
22	D o° ♅	8am 5	3	40
22	D o° Ψ	0pm56	4	51
24	☿ σ h	9am58	0	14
25	D o° h	11am 7	6	2
25	D o° ☿	1pm12	6	20
26	D o° ⊙	0am 4	5	29
27	D o° ⊙	11am10	3	31
28	D o° ♀	4pm 9	3	2
29	D o° ♃	9pm34	2	17
30	D σ ♇	9pm 7	13	41

APRIL

Day	Aspect	Time	°	′
3	D σ Ψ	9pm15	3	45
4	D σ ♅	2am26	4	57
4	☿ σ ♂	8pm43	1	15
7	D σ h	10am30	6	4
8	D σ ⊙	8pm59	5	4
9	D σ ☿	4am29	6	9
11	D σ ⊙	0am17	2	38
11	♀ σ ♃	2pm53	1	12
12	D o° ♃	7pm 7	2	22
12	D • ♀	10pm42	0	58
14	D o° ♇	2am51	13	42
18	D o° Ψ	4pm23	3	51
18	D o° ♅	9pm53	5	3
22	D o° h	1am54	6	8
23	D o° ♇	11pm 7	4	27
24	♀ σ ♇	1am48	14	27
25	D o° ☿	10am11	3	3
25	D o° ♀	7pm45	1	35
28	D σ ♃	3am34	2	30
27	D σ ♇	6am24	13	44
27	D σ ⊙	1pm19	1	15
2	⊙ σ ♃	8am55	1	20
30	☿ σ ♃	9am39	1	5
30	☿ σ ☿	10am21	0	14

MAY

Day	Aspect	Time	°	′
1	D σ Ψ	4am36	3	53
1	D σ ♅	9am59	5	6
4	D σ h	9pm11	6	10
8	D σ ♂	0am17	3	44
8	☿ σ ♂	9am50	15	9
9	D σ ♃	6pm20	2	38
10	D • ●	5pm 7	0	21
10	D o° ♇	7am25	13	47
11	D σ ☿	9pm58	2	33
13	D σ ♀	7am 2	3	37
15	D o° Ψ	10pm15	3	53
16	D o° ♅	3am56	5	7
17	⊙ o° ♇	8pm21	14	3
19	D o° h	1pm27	6	11
22	D o° ♂	8pm32	2	50
23	D σ ♃	9am 5	2	43
24	D σ ♇	4pm 8	13	47
25	D • ●	3am39	0	54
26	D o° ☿	6pm52	5	7
27	D o° ♀	11am 1	5	21
28	D o° Ψ	1pm13	3	52
28	D σ ♅	6pm22	5	6

JUNE

Day	Aspect	Time	°	′
1	♂ o° ♃	4am36	0	33
1	D σ h	7am 4	6	12
5	D o° ♃	7pm 2	2	46
6	D σ ♂	3am15	1	52
7	D o° ♇	0pm17	13	46
9	♀ o° Ψ	5am42	2	31
9	D σ ⊙	8am26	2	10
10	D σ ☿	11pm23	3	13
11	♀ o° ♅	3pm 6	1	25
12	D o° Ψ	2am57	3	49
12	D o° ♅	8am20	5	3
12	D σ ♀	10am 8	6	30
15	D σ h	9pm11	6	10
19	D σ ♃	2pm36	2	44
20	D σ ♂	4pm 0	0	47
21	D o° ♇	0am42	13	42
23	D o° ♅	11am33	3	14
23	D o° ☿	4pm17	0	23
24	D o° Ψ	10pm16	3	47
25	D o° h	2am56	5	11
25	⊙ σ ☿	9am57	4	8
26	D o° ♀	9am51	6	42
27	♂ o° ♇	9pm 3	13	25
28	D σ h	3pm57	6	10

JULY

Day	Aspect	Time	°	′
3	D o° ♃	0am 5	2	38
4	D o° ♇	6pm15	13	35
5	D • ♂	5am 1	0	20
7	D σ ☿	1pm13	1	21
7	D σ ⊙	9pm37	4	6
9	D o° Ψ	8am 8	3	44
9	D o° ♅	0pm53	4	57
10	D σ ♂	6am50	6	3
13	D o° h	2am 5	6	8
14	⊙ o° Ψ	3pm32	0	37
14	D σ ♀	9pm12	2	27
16	D o° ♂	9pm 2	2	10
17	⊙ o° ♅	3am54	0	31
18	D σ ♇	7am23	13	25
19	D o° ☿	9am20	1	26
21	D o° ♀	7am44	1	59
21	♀ σ h	5pm58	0	51
22	D σ ♅	6am26	3	43
22	D σ ♃	10am33	4	56
22	D o° ⊙	8pm16	4	35
25	D σ h	11pm17	6	7
26	D o° ♀	9am17	4	48
29	☿ o° Ψ	8pm22	0	49
30	D o° ♃	10am16	2	13
31	☿ o° ♅	1am40	0	5

AUGUST

Day	Aspect	Time	°	′
1	D o° ♇	1am33	13	12
3	D σ ♂	4am48	2	33
5	D o° Ψ	2pm44	3	45
5	D o° ♅	6pm48	4	57
6	D σ ⊙	7pm36	6	6
7	D σ ⊙	8am45	4	47
9	D o° h	6am12	6	7
10	D σ ♀	8pm54	2	48
13	⊙ σ ☿	0am54	1	40
13	D σ ♃	6am17	1	56
14	D σ ♇	0pm52	12	57
17	D o° ♂	0am33	3	30
18	D σ Ψ	0pm55	3	47
18	D σ ♅	4pm31	4	59
21	D o° ⊙	6am47	4	39
22	D o° ☿	0am23	5	46
23	☿ σ h	4am35	6	9
23	☿ o° h	4am55	0	32
25	D o° ♀	5am50	0	30
25	D o° ♃	0am34	1	38
28	D o° ♇	9am49	12	42

SEPTEMBER

Day	Aspect	Time	°	′
1	D σ ♂	1am59	4	25
1	⊙ σ h	4pm40	1	50
1	D o° Ψ	10pm42	3	53
2	D o° ♅	2am17	5	3
5	D o° h	11am24	6	12
5	D σ ⊙	6pm33	4	12
7	D σ ♀	6am44	2	52
9	D σ ☿	2am19	2	9
9	D σ ♃	6pm59	1	19
10	D o° ♇	7pm 5	12	28
14	D σ ♂	1pm39	5	6
14	D σ Ψ	6pm 2	3	58
14	D σ ♅	9pm19	5	8
18	D σ h	8am 3	6	15
18	♂ o° Ψ	2pm21	1	18
19	D o° ⊙	8pm 1	3	34
21	♂ o° ♅	2pm55	0	15
22	D o° ☿	2am46	0	22
23	D o° ♀	1pm 7	4	43
23	D o° ☿	5pm27	1	0
24	D o° ♇	6pm28	12	15
29	D o° Ψ	7am12	4	4
29	D o° ♅	10am38	5	14
29	D σ ♂	7pm46	5	44
29	♀ σ ♃	9pm51	6	33

OCTOBER

Day	Aspect	Time	°	′
2	D o° h	6pm22	6	20
3	D σ ⊙	3am55	2	39
6	D σ ♀	7pm12	2	32
7	D • ♃	11am39	0	42
7	D σ ♀	1pm20	6	35
7	D σ ♇	3am51	12	5
11	D σ Ψ	11pm26	4	9
12	D σ ♅	2am40	5	17
12	D σ ⊙	0am30	6	9
15	♀ σ ♃	4am13	7	32
15	D σ h	11am 2	6	22
19	D o° ♇	0pm18	1	36
19	D o° ♀	7pm15	0	15
21	⊙ σ ☿	5am17	1	8
21	D o° ♃	11am36	0	23
22	D o° ♇	3am 0	11	56
26	D o° Ψ	3pm14	4	13
26	D o° ♅	6pm57	5	20
28	D σ ♂	8am50	6	31
30	D o° h	2am32	6	24

DISTANCES APART OF ALL ☌s AND ☍s IN 1994

Note: The Distances Apart are in Declination

NOVEMBER

2	☽ ☌ ☿	7am 4	3 46
2	☉ ☌ ♀	11pm12	5 7
3	☽ ☌ ♀	0pm 8	4 35
3	☽ ● ●	1pm36	0 21
4	☽ ● ♃	7am31	0 6
4	☽ ☌ ♇	3pm33	11 51
8	☽ ☌ ♆	7am 8	4 14
8	☽ ☌ ♅	10am37	5 21
10	☽ ☍ ♂	8am16	6 45
11	☽ ☌ ♄	3pm45	6 23
13	☿ ☌ ♀	6pm 1	4 30
16	☽ ☍ ♀	9am59	1 2
16	☽ ☍ ☿	9pm24	2 6
17	☉ ☌ ♃	7pm48	0 46
18	☽ ☍ ♃	6am12	0 11
18	☽ ☍ ☉	6am57	0 58
18	☽ ☍ ♇	11am23	11 47
20	☉ ☌ ♇	0pm51	12 57
22	☽ ☍ ♆	10pm34	4 14
23	☽ ☍ ♅	2am55	5 20
25	☽ ☌ ♂	2pm47	6 59
26	☽ ☍ ♄	10am57	6 19
28	☿ ☌ ♃	4pm40	0 22
29	☿ ☌ ♇	2am53	12 37
30	☽ ☌ ♀	0pm51	1 52

DECEMBER

2	☽ ● ♃	4am43	0 28
2	☽ ☌ ♇	4am44	11 44
2	♃ ☌ ♇	7am24	12 12
2	☽ ☌ ☿	1pm 2	1 44
2	☽ ☌ ☉	11pm54	2 16
5	☽ ☌ ♆	5pm55	4 13
5	☽ ☌ ♅	9pm56	5 19
8	☽ ☍ ♂	10am33	7 12
9	☽ ☌ ♄	0am13	6 13
14	☉ ☌ ☿	3am16	1 15
14	☽ ☍ ♀	4am45	3 0
15	☽ ☍ ♇	7pm53	11 42
16	☽ ☍ ♃	0am53	0 45
18	☽ ☍ ☉	2am17	3 26
18	☽ ☍ ☿	7am23	5 12
20	☽ ☍ ♆	5am59	4 10
20	☽ ☍ ♅	11am12	5 16
23	☽ ☌ ♂	9am42	7 29
23	☽ ☍ ♄	7pm35	6 3
29	☽ ☌ ♀	3am36	2 46
29	☽ ☌ ♇	4pm52	11 39
30	☽ ● ♃	0am46	1 3

TIME WHEN THE SUN, MOON AND PLANETS ENTER THE ZODIACAL SIGNS IN 1994

JANUARY

1	☽ ♍	8pm14
3	☽ ♎	11pm31
6	☽ ♏	2am29
8	☽ ♐	5am34
10	☽ ♑	9am16
12	☽ ♒	2pm26
14	☿ ♒	0am25
14	☽ ♓	10pm 4
17	☽ ♈	8am42
19	♀ ♒	4pm28
19	☽ ♉	9pm22
20	☉ ♒	7am 7
22	☽ ♊	9am34
24	☽ ♋	6pm54
27	☽ ♌	0am38
28	♂ ♒	4am 5
28	♄ ♓	11pm43
29	☽ ♍	3am38
31	☽ ♎	5am34

FEBRUARY

1	☿ ♓	10am29
2	☽ ♏	7am50
4	☽ ♐	11am15
6	☽ ♑	4pm 2
8	☽ ♒	10pm17
11	☽ ♓	6am23
12	♀ ♓	2pm 4
13	☽ ♈	4pm50
16	☽ ♉	5am20
18	☽ ♊	6pm 5
18	☉ ♓	9pm22
21	☽ ♋	4am26
21	☿ ♒	3pm16
23	☽ ♌	10am47
25	☽ ♍	1pm27
27	☽ ♎	2pm 6

MARCH

1	☽ ♏	2pm44
3	☽ ♐	4pm54
5	☽ ♑	9pm25
7	♂ ♓	11am 1
8	☽ ♒	4am16
8	♀ ♈	2pm28
10	☽ ♓	1pm10
12	☽ ♈	11pm59
15	☽ ♉	0pm27
18	☽ ♊	1am29
18	☿ ♓	0pm 3
20	☽ ♋	0pm53
20	☉ ♈	8pm28
22	☽ ♌	8pm38
25	☽ ♍	0am14
27	☽ ♎	0am46
29	☽ ♏	0am15
31	☽ ♐	0am41

APRIL

1	♀ ♉	7pm20
2	☽ ♑	3am39
4	☽ ♒	9am46
6	☽ ♓	6pm52
9	☽ ♈	6am 9
9	☿ ♈	4pm29
11	☽ ♉	6pm48
14	☽ ♊	7am47
14	♂ ♈	6pm 2
16	☽ ♋	7pm40
19	☽ ♌	4am43
20	☉ ♉	7am36
21	☽ ♍	9am57
23	☽ ♎	11am40
25	☽ ♏	11am18
25	☿ ♉	6pm27
26	♀ ♊	6am24
27	☽ ♐	10am48
29	☽ ♑	0pm 5

MAY

1	☽ ♒	4pm36
4	☽ ♓	0am47
6	☽ ♈	0pm 1
9	☽ ♉	0am50
9	☿ ♊	9pm 9
11	☽ ♊	1pm43
14	☽ ♋	1am27
16	☽ ♌	10am58
18	☽ ♍	5pm29
20	☽ ♎	8pm54
21	♀ ♋	1am26
21	☉ ♊	6am49
22	☽ ♏	9pm50
23	♂ ♉	10pm37
24	☽ ♐	9pm43
26	☽ ♑	10pm17
28	☿ ♋	2pm54
29	☽ ♒	1am19
31	☽ ♓	8am 4

JUNE

2	☽ ♈	6pm32
5	☽ ♉	7am14
7	☽ ♊	8pm 3
10	☽ ♋	7am21
12	☽ ♌	4pm28
14	☽ ♍	11pm16
15	♀ ♌	7am23
17	☽ ♎	3am47
19	☽ ♏	6am19
21	☽ ♐	7am32
21	☉ ♋	2pm48
23	☽ ♑	8am37
25	☽ ♒	11am10
27	☽ ♓	4pm46
30	☽ ♈	2am 7

JULY

2	☽ ♉	2pm23
2	☿ ♊	11pm20
3	♂ ♊	10pm30
5	☽ ♊	3am12
7	☽ ♋	2pm17
9	☽ ♌	10pm43
10	☿ ♋	0pm38
11	♀ ♍	6am33
12	☽ ♍	4am48
14	☽ ♎	9am14
16	☽ ♏	0pm35
18	☽ ♐	3pm 9
20	☽ ♑	5pm31
22	☽ ♒	8pm39
23	☉ ♌	1am41
25	☽ ♓	1am57
27	☽ ♈	10am31
29	☽ ♉	10pm13

AUGUST

1	☽ ♊	11am 5
3	☿ ♌	6am 9
3	☽ ♋	10pm22
6	☽ ♌	6am30
7	♀ ♎	2pm36
8	☽ ♍	11am42
10	☽ ♎	3pm 6
12	☽ ♏	5pm56
14	☽ ♐	8pm53
16	♂ ♋	7pm15
17	☽ ♑	0am18
18	☿ ♍	0am44
19	☽ ♒	4am34
21	☽ ♓	10am28
23	☉ ♍	8am44
23	☽ ♈	6pm56
26	☽ ♉	6am14
28	☽ ♊	7pm 7
31	☽ ♋	6am59

SEPTEMBER

2	☽ ♌	3pm36
4	☿ ♎	4am56
4	☽ ♍	8pm33
6	☽ ♎	10pm56
7	♀ ♏	5pm13
9	☽ ♏	0am26
11	☽ ♐	2am25
13	☽ ♑	5am45
15	☽ ♒	10am43
17	☽ ♓	5pm32
20	☽ ♈	2am30
22	☽ ♉	1pm48
23	☉ ♎	6am19
25	☽ ♊	2am41
27	☿ ♏	8am52
27	☽ ♋	3pm11
30	☽ ♌	0am55

OCTOBER

2	☽ ♍	6am38
4	☽ ♎	8am55
4	♂ ♌	3pm48
6	☽ ♏	9am22
8	☽ ♐	9am47
10	☽ ♑	11am44
12	☽ ♒	4pm10
14	☽ ♓	11pm18
17	☽ ♈	8am57
19	☿ ♎	6am17
19	☽ ♉	8pm35
22	☽ ♊	9am28
23	☉ ♏	3pm36
24	☽ ♋	10pm15
27	☽ ♌	9am 4
29	☽ ♍	4pm20
31	☽ ♎	7pm45

NOVEMBER

2	☽ ♏	8pm19
4	☽ ♐	7pm46
6	☽ ♑	8pm 3
8	☽ ♒	10pm49
10	☿ ♏	0pm46
11	☽ ♓	5am 5
13	☽ ♈	2pm44
16	☽ ♉	2am44
18	☽ ♊	3pm41
21	☽ ♋	4am21
22	☉ ♐	1pm 6
23	☽ ♌	3pm32
26	☽ ♍	0am 9
28	☽ ♎	5am21
30	☿ ♐	4am38
30	☽ ♏	7am21

DECEMBER

2	☽ ♐	7am13
4	☽ ♑	6am43
6	☽ ♒	7am53
8	☽ ♓	0pm24
9	♃ ♐	10am54
10	☽ ♈	9pm 4
12	♂ ♍	11am32
13	☽ ♉	8am56
15	☽ ♊	10pm 0
18	☽ ♋	10am24
19	☿ ♑	6am25
20	☽ ♌	9pm12
22	☉ ♑	2am23
23	☽ ♍	6am 0
25	☽ ♎	0pm27
27	☽ ♏	4pm16
29	☽ ♐	5pm45
31	☽ ♑	5pm58

LOCAL MEAN TIME OF SUNRISE FOR LATITUDES
60° North to 50° South
FOR ALL SUNDAYS IN 1994.   (ALL TIMES ARE A.M.)

Date	LON-DON	NORTHERN LATITUDES 60°	55°	50°	40°	30°	20°	10°	0°	SOUTHERN LATITUDES 10°	20°	30°	40°	50°
1994	H M	H M	H M	H M	H M	H M	H M	H M	H M	H M	H M	H M	H M	H M
Jan. 2	8 6	9 3	8 25	7 59	7 22	6 56	6 35	6 17	6 0	5 43	5 25	5 3	4 36	3 56
,, 9	8 4	8 57	8 22	7 57	7 22	6 57	6 37	6 20	6 3	5 47	5 29	5 8	4 42	4 4
,, 16	7 59	8 48	8 16	7 53	7 20	6 57	6 38	6 22	6 6	5 51	5 34	5 15	4 50	4 15
,, 23	7 52	8 36	8 7	7 46	7 17	6 55	6 38	6 23	6 8	5 54	5 39	5 21	4 58	4 26
,, 30	7 43	8 21	7 56	7 38	7 11	6 52	6 36	6 23	6 10	5 57	5 42	5 26	5 5	4 36
Feb. 6	7 32	8 4	7 43	7 28	7 5	6 48	6 34	6 22	6 11	5 59	5 47	5 33	5 15	4 50
,, 13	7 20	7 46	7 29	7 16	6 57	6 42	6 31	6 20	6 11	6 1	5 50	5 38	5 22	5 1
,, 20	7 6	7 27	7 13	7 3	6 48	6 36	6 27	6 18	6 10	6 3	5 54	5 44	5 32	5 15
,, 27	6 51	7 7	6 57	6 49	6 38	6 29	6 22	6 16	6 10	6 4	5 57	5 49	5 40	5 26
Mar. 6	6 36	6 46	6 40	6 35	6 27	6 22	6 17	6 12	6 8	6 4	6 0	5 54	5 47	5 38
,, 13	6 21	6 26	6 22	6 20	6 16	6 14	6 11	6 9	6 6	6 4	6 1	5 58	5 54	5 48
,, 20	6 5	6 4	6 5	6 5	6 5	6 5	6 5	6 5	6 4	6 4	6 4	6 3	6 1	6 0
,, 27	5 49	5 43	5 46	5 50	5 54	5 56	5 59	6 1	6 2	6 4	6 5	6 7	6 9	6 12
Apr. 3	5 33	5 22	5 29	5 34	5 42	5 48	5 53	5 57	6 0	6 3	6 7	6 11	6 16	6 23
,, 10	5 17	5 2	5 11	5 20	5 31	5 40	5 47	5 53	5 58	6 3	6 9	6 15	6 22	6 32
,, 17	5 2	4 40	4 54	5 5	5 21	5 32	5 41	5 49	5 56	6 4	6 11	6 19	6 30	6 43
,, 24	4 47	4 20	4 37	4 51	5 10	5 25	5 36	5 46	5 55	6 4	6 13	6 24	6 36	6 54
May 1	4 34	4 0	4 22	4 38	5 1	5 18	5 31	5 43	5 54	6 4	6 15	6 28	6 43	7 5
,, 8	4 21	3 41	4 7	4 26	4 53	5 12	5 27	5 41	5 53	6 5	6 18	6 32	6 50	7 15
,, 15	4 9	3 24	3 54	4 15	4 46	5 7	5 24	5 39	5 53	6 6	6 21	6 37	6 58	7 26
,, 22	3 59	3 8	3 42	4 6	4 40	5 3	5 22	5 38	5 53	6 8	6 23	6 41	7 3	7 34
,, 29	3 52	2 55	3 32	3 59	4 35	5 0	5 20	5 37	5 53	6 10	6 27	6 46	7 10	7 43
June 5	3 46	2 45	3 26	3 54	4 32	4 58	5 20	5 38	5 54	6 11	6 29	6 49	7 14	7 49
,, 12	3 43	2 38	3 21	3 51	4 30	4 58	5 20	5 38	5 56	6 14	6 32	6 53	7 19	7 56
,, 19	3 42	2 35	3 20	3 50	4 30	4 59	5 21	5 40	5 57	6 15	6 34	6 55	7 21	7 59
,, 26	3 44	2 37	3 21	3 52	4 32	5 0	5 22	5 41	5 59	6 16	6 34	6 56	7 22	8 0
July 3	3 48	2 43	3 26	3 55	4 35	5 3	5 24	5 43	6 0	6 17	6 35	6 56	7 22	7 59
,, 10	3 54	2 53	3 33	4 1	4 39	5 6	5 27	5 45	6 1	6 17	6 35	6 55	7 20	7 56
,, 17	4 1	3 5	3 42	4 8	4 44	5 10	5 29	5 46	6 2	6 18	6 35	6 54	7 18	7 51
,, 24	4 10	3 20	3 54	4 17	4 50	5 13	5 32	5 48	6 3	6 17	6 33	6 51	7 13	7 43
,, 31	4 21	3 36	4 5	4 26	4 56	5 18	5 34	5 49	6 3	6 16	6 30	6 46	7 6	7 33
Aug. 7	4 32	3 53	4 18	4 36	5 3	5 22	5 37	5 50	6 2	6 14	6 27	6 42	7 0	7 24
,, 14	4 42	4 10	4 31	4 46	5 10	5 26	5 39	5 51	6 1	6 11	6 22	6 35	6 50	7 11
,, 21	4 53	4 26	4 44	4 57	5 16	5 30	5 41	5 51	6 0	6 8	6 18	6 28	6 41	6 58
,, 28	5 5	4 43	4 56	5 7	5 23	5 34	5 43	5 51	5 58	6 5	6 13	6 21	6 32	6 45
Sept. 4	5 16	5 0	5 10	5 18	5 29	5 38	5 45	5 51	5 56	6 1	6 7	6 13	6 20	6 30
,, 11	5 27	5 16	5 23	5 28	5 36	5 42	5 46	5 50	5 54	5 57	6 0	6 4	6 9	6 15
,, 18	5 38	5 33	5 36	5 39	5 43	5 46	5 48	5 50	5 51	5 52	5 53	5 55	5 57	5 59
,, 25	5 49	5 49	5 49	5 49	5 49	5 49	5 49	5 49	5 49	5 48	5 47	5 46	5 45	5 43
Oct. 2	6 1	6 6	6 2	6 0	5 56	5 53	5 51	5 49	5 46	5 45	5 42	5 39	5 35	5 30
,, 9	6 12	6 22	6 16	6 11	6 3	5 58	5 53	5 48	5 44	5 40	5 36	5 30	5 24	5 15
,, 16	6 24	6 40	6 30	6 22	6 10	6 2	5 55	5 49	5 42	5 36	5 29	5 21	5 12	4 58
,, 23	6 36	6 57	6 43	6 33	6 18	6 7	5 57	5 49	5 41	5 33	5 24	5 14	5 1	4 44
,, 30	6 49	7 15	6 58	6 45	6 26	6 12	6 0	5 50	5 40	5 30	5 20	5 8	4 52	4 31
Nov. 6	7 0	7 33	7 12	6 56	6 34	6 17	6 4	5 52	5 40	5 29	5 17	5 2	4 44	4 20
,, 13	7 13	7 51	7 26	7 8	6 42	6 23	6 7	5 54	5 41	5 28	5 14	4 58	4 38	4 9
,, 20	7 25	8 8	7 40	7 20	6 50	6 29	6 12	5 56	5 42	5 27	5 12	4 54	4 31	3 59
,, 27	7 36	8 25	7 53	7 30	6 58	6 34	6 16	6 0	5 44	5 29	5 12	4 52	4 28	3 53
Dec. 4	7 47	8 39	8 4	7 40	7 5	6 40	6 20	6 3	5 46	5 30	5 12	4 51	4 25	3 48
,, 11	7 55	8 51	8 14	7 48	7 11	6 45	6 25	6 6	5 49	5 32	5 14	4 52	4 25	3 45
,, 18	8 1	9 0	8 21	7 54	7 16	6 50	6 29	6 10	5 53	5 35	5 16	4 54	4 26	3 46
,, 25	8 5	9 4	8 25	7 58	7 20	6 53	6 32	6 14	5 56	5 39	5 20	4 58	4 30	3 49
1995 Jan. 1	8 6	9 3	8 25	7 59	7 22	6 56	6 35	6 17	5 59	5 41	5 23	5 1	4 33	3 54

Example:—To find the time of Sunrise in Jamaica (Latitude 18° N.) on Friday, July 1st, 1994. On June 26th, L.M.T. = 5h. 22m. + $\frac{2}{10}$ × 19m. = 5h. 26m., on July 3rd L.M.T. = 5h. 24m. + $\frac{7}{10}$ × 19m. = 5h. 28m., therefore L.M.T. on July 1st = 5h. 26m. + $\frac{5}{7}$ × 2m. = 5h. 27m. A.M.

LOCAL MEAN TIME OF SUNSET FOR LATITUDES
60° North to 50° South
FOR ALL SUNDAYS IN 1994.   (ALL TIMES ARE P.M.)

Date	LON-DON	NORTHERN LATITUDES 60°	55°	50°	40°	30°	20°	10°	0°	SOUTHERN LATITUDES 10°	20°	30°	40°	50°
1994	H M	H M	H M	H M	H M	H M	H M	H M	H M	H M	H M	H M	H M	H M
Jan. 2	4 2	3 6	3 43	4 9	4 46	5 12	5 32	5 51	6 8	6 25	6 43	7 5	7 32	8 12
,, 9	4 10	3 18	3 53	4 17	4 52	5 17	5 37	5 54	6 11	6 27	6 45	7 6	7 32	8 10
,, 16	4 21	3 33	4 4	4 27	5 0	5 23	5 42	5 58	6 13	6 29	6 46	7 5	7 30	8 5
,, 23	4 32	3 49	4 17	4 38	5 8	5 29	5 46	6 1	6 15	6 30	6 46	7 4	7 26	7 58
,, 30	4 45	4 7	4 31	4 50	5 16	5 35	5 50	6 4	6 17	6 29	6 44	7 0	7 21	7 49
Feb. 6	4 58	4 26	4 46	5 2	5 24	5 41	5 54	6 6	6 18	6 29	6 41	6 55	7 13	7 38
,, 13	5 10	4 44	5 1	5 14	5 33	5 46	5 58	6 8	6 18	6 27	6 38	6 50	7 5	7 26
,, 20	5 23	5 2	5 16	5 26	5 41	5 52	6 1	6 10	6 17	6 25	6 34	6 43	6 56	7 12
,, 27	5 36	5 20	5 30	5 38	5 49	5 57	6 4	6 10	6 16	6 22	6 29	6 36	6 46	6 59
Mar. 6	5 48	5 38	5 44	5 49	5 56	6 2	6 7	6 11	6 15	6 19	6 24	6 29	6 36	6 45
,, 13	6 0	5 55	5 58	6 0	6 4	6 6	6 9	6 11	6 13	6 15	6 17	6 20	6 24	6 30
,, 20	6 12	6 12	6 12	6 12	6 11	6 11	6 11	6 11	6 11	6 11	6 12	6 13	6 14	6 15
,, 27	6 24	6 29	6 25	6 23	6 18	6 16	6 13	6 11	6 9	6 7	6 5	6 3	6 0	5 57
Apr. 3	6 35	6 46	6 39	6 34	6 25	6 19	6 15	6 10	6 7	6 3	5 59	5 54	5 49	5 42
,, 10	6 47	7 4	6 53	6 45	6 32	6 24	6 16	6 10	6 5	5 59	5 54	5 47	5 40	5 30
,, 17	6 59	7 21	7 6	6 56	6 40	6 28	6 19	6 10	6 3	5 56	5 49	5 40	5 29	5 16
,, 24	7 10	7 38	7 20	7 6	6 46	6 32	6 21	6 11	6 2	5 52	5 43	5 32	5 19	5 1
May 1	7 21	7 55	7 34	7 17	6 54	6 37	6 23	6 11	6 1	5 49	5 38	5 25	5 9	4 48
,, 8	7 33	8 13	7 47	7 28	7 1	6 41	6 26	6 12	6 0	5 47	5 34	5 19	5 1	4 36
,, 15	7 44	8 30	8 0	7 38	7 8	6 46	6 28	6 14	6 0	5 46	5 31	5 14	4 54	4 25
,, 22	7 54	8 46	8 11	7 47	7 14	6 50	6 31	6 15	6 0	5 45	5 29	5 11	4 49	4 18
,, 29	8 3	9 0	8 22	7 56	7 20	6 54	6 34	6 17	6 1	5 45	5 28	5 9	4 45	4 11
June 5	8 10	9 12	8 31	8 3	7 25	6 58	6 37	6 19	6 2	5 45	5 27	5 7	4 42	4 6
,, 12	8 16	9 22	8 38	8 9	7 29	7 1	6 39	6 20	6 3	5 46	5 28	5 7	4 41	4 4
,, 19	8 20	9 27	8 42	8 12	7 32	7 3	6 41	6 22	6 5	5 48	5 29	5 8	4 41	4 4
,, 26	8 21	9 28	8 43	8 13	7 33	7 5	6 43	6 24	6 6	5 49	5 30	5 9	4 42	4 5
July 3	8 19	9 24	8 41	8 12	7 32	7 5	6 43	6 25	6 8	5 50	5 32	5 11	4 45	4 8
,, 10	8 15	9 16	8 36	8 8	7 30	7 4	6 43	6 25	6 9	5 52	5 34	5 14	4 49	4 14
,, 17	8 10	9 5	8 29	8 3	7 27	7 2	6 42	6 25	6 9	5 55	5 38	5 19	4 56	4 23
,, 24	8 2	8 51	8 18	7 55	7 22	6 59	6 40	6 24	6 10	5 56	5 40	5 22	5 0	4 30
,, 31	7 51	8 35	8 6	7 45	7 16	6 54	6 38	6 23	6 10	5 56	5 42	5 26	5 7	4 39
Aug. 7	7 39	8 17	7 52	7 34	7 8	6 49	6 34	6 21	6 9	5 58	5 45	5 30	5 13	4 48
,, 14	7 26	7 58	7 37	7 22	6 59	6 43	6 30	6 18	6 8	5 58	5 46	5 34	5 19	4 58
,, 21	7 12	7 39	7 21	7 8	6 50	6 36	6 25	6 15	6 6	5 58	5 49	5 39	5 26	5 10
,, 28	6 57	7 18	7 4	6 54	6 39	6 28	6 19	6 12	6 5	5 58	5 51	5 42	5 32	5 19
Sept. 4	6 41	6 57	6 47	6 40	6 28	6 20	6 13	6 8	6 2	5 57	5 52	5 46	5 39	5 29
,, 11	6 25	6 36	6 29	6 24	6 17	6 11	6 7	6 4	6 0	5 57	5 54	5 50	5 46	5 40
,, 18	6 10	6 15	6 11	6 9	6 5	6 3	6 1	5 59	5 58	5 56	5 55	5 53	5 52	5 50
,, 25	5 54	5 53	5 53	5 54	5 54	5 54	5 54	5 55	5 55	5 56	5 57	5 57	5 58	5 59
Oct. 2	5 37	5 32	5 36	5 38	5 42	5 45	5 48	5 50	5 53	5 56	5 58	6 1	6 5	6 11
,, 9	5 22	5 11	5 18	5 23	5 31	5 37	5 42	5 46	5 51	5 55	6 0	6 6	6 12	6 22
,, 16	5 7	4 51	5 0	5 9	5 20	5 29	5 36	5 43	5 49	5 55	6 2	6 10	6 20	6 34
,, 23	4 52	4 31	4 44	4 55	5 10	5 22	5 31	5 40	5 48	5 56	6 5	6 15	6 27	6 45
,, 30	4 38	4 12	4 29	4 42	5 1	5 15	5 27	5 37	5 47	5 57	6 8	6 20	6 36	6 57
Nov. 6	4 26	3 53	4 14	4 30	4 53	5 10	5 24	5 36	5 47	5 59	6 11	6 26	6 44	7 9
,, 13	4 15	3 37	4 1	4 20	4 46	5 6	5 21	5 35	5 48	6 1	6 15	6 31	6 52	7 20
,, 20	4 5	3 22	3 50	4 11	4 41	5 2	5 20	5 35	5 49	6 3	6 19	6 37	7 0	7 33
,, 27	3 58	3 10	3 41	4 4	4 37	5 0	5 19	5 36	5 51	6 7	6 24	6 43	7 8	7 43
Dec. 4	3 53	3 0	3 35	4 0	4 35	5 0	5 20	5 37	5 54	6 10	6 28	6 48	7 15	7 52
,, 11	3 51	2 54	3 32	3 58	4 35	5 1	5 22	5 40	5 57	6 14	6 33	6 54	7 22	8 1
,, 18	3 52	2 53	3 32	3 59	4 36	5 3	5 24	5 43	6 0	6 18	6 37	6 59	7 27	8 7
,, 25	3 55	2 56	3 35	4 2	4 40	5 6	5 28	5 46	6 4	6 22	6 40	7 3	7 31	8 11
1995 Jan. 1	4 0	3 4	3 42	4 8	4 45	5 11	5 32	5 50	6 7	6 24	6 42	7 4	7 32	8 12

Example:—To find the time of Sunset in Canberra (Latitude 35°·3 S.) on Wednesday, August 3rd, 1994. On July 31st, L.M.T. = 5h. 26m. − 5/8 × 19m. = 5h. 16m., on August 7th, L.M.T. = 5h. 30m. − 5/8 × 17m. = 5h. 21m., therefore L.M.T. on August 3rd = 5h. 16m. + 4/7 × 5m. = 5h. 18m. P.M.

TABLES OF HOUSES FOR LONDON, Latitude 51° 32' N.

Sidereal Time	10 ♈	11 ♉	12 ♊	Ascen ♋	2 ♌	3 ♍
H. M. S.	°	°	°	° °	°	°
0 0 0	0	9	22	26 36	12	3
0 3 40	1	10	23	27 17	13	3
0 7 20	2	11	24	27 56	14	4
0 11 0	3	12	25	28 42	15	5
0 14 41	4	13	25	29 17	15	6
0 18 21	5	14	26	29 55	16	7
0 22 2	6	15	27	0♌ 34	17	8
0 25 42	7	16	28	1 14	18	8
0 29 23	8	17	29	1 55	19	9
0 33 4	9	18	0♋	2 33	19	10
0 36 45	10	19	1	3 14	20	11
0 40 26	11	20	1	3 54	20	12
0 44 8	12	21	2	4 33	21	13
0 47 50	13	22	3	5 12	22	14
0 51 32	14	23	4	5 52	23	15
0 55 14	15	24	5	6 30	23	15
0 58 57	16	25	6	7 9	24	16
1 2 40	17	26	6	7 50	25	17
1 6 23	18	27	7	8 30	26	18
1 10 7	19	28	8	9 9	26	19
1 13 51	20	29	9	9 48	27	19
1 17 35	21	0♊	10	10 28	28	20
1 21 20	22	1	10	11 8	28	21
1 25 6	23	2	11	11 48	29	22
1 28 52	24	3	12	12 28	0♍	23
1 32 38	25	4	13	13 8	1	24
1 36 25	26	5	14	13 48	1	25
1 40 12	27	6	14	14 28	2	25
1 44 0	28	7	15	15 8	3	26
1 47 48	29	8	16	15 48	4	27
1 51 37	30	9	17	16 28	4	28

Sidereal Time	10 ♉	11 ♊	12 ♋	Ascen ♌	2 ♍	3 ♍
H. M. S.	°	°	°	° °	°	°
1 51 37	0	9	17	16 28	4	28
1 55 27	1	10	18	17 8	5	29
1 59 17	2	11	19	17 48	6	0♎
2 3 8	3	12	19	18 28	7	1
2 6 59	4	13	20	19 8	8	2
2 10 51	5	14	21	19 49	9	2
2 14 44	6	15	22	20 29	9	3
2 18 37	7	16	22	21 10	10	4
2 22 31	8	17	23	21 51	11	5
2 26 25	9	18	24	22 32	11	6
2 30 20	10	19	25	23 14	12	7
2 34 16	11	20	25	23 55	13	8
2 38 13	12	21	26	24 36	14	9
2 42 10	13	22	27	25 17	15	10
2 46 8	14	23	28	25 58	15	11
2 50 7	15	24	29	26 40	16	12
2 54 7	16	25	29	27 22	17	12
2 58 7	17	26	0♌	28 4	18	13
3 2 8	18	27	1	28 46	18	14
3 6 9	19	27	2	29 28	19	15
3 10 12	20	28	3	0♍ 12	20	16
3 14 15	21	29	3	0 54	21	17
3 18 19	22	0♋	4	1 36	22	18
3 22 23	23	1	5	2 20	23	19
3 26 29	24	2	6	3 2	23	20
3 30 35	25	3	7	3 45	24	21
3 34 41	26	4	7	4 28	25	22
3 38 49	27	5	8	5 11	26	23
3 42 57	28	6	9	5 54	27	24
3 47 6	29	7	10	6 38	27	25
3 51 15	30	8	11	7 21	28	25

Sidereal Time	10 ♊	11 ♋	12 ♌	Ascen ♍	2 ♍	3 ♎
H. M. S.	°	°	°	° °	°	°
3 51 15	0	8	11	7 21	28	25
3 55 25	1	9	12	8 5	29	26
3 59 36	2	10	12	8 49	0♎	27
4 3 48	3	10	13	9 33	1	28
4 8 0	4	11	14	10 17	2	29
4 12 13	5	12	15	11 2	2	0♏
4 16 26	6	13	16	11 46	3	1
4 20 40	7	14	17	12 30	4	2
4 24 55	8	15	17	13 15	5	3
4 29 10	9	16	18	14 0	6	4
4 33 26	10	17	19	14 45	7	5
4 37 42	11	18	20	15 30	8	6
4 41 59	12	19	21	16 15	8	7
4 46 16	13	20	21	17 0	9	8
4 50 34	14	21	22	17 45	10	9
4 54 52	15	22	23	18 30	11	10
4 59 10	16	23	24	19 16	12	11
5 3 29	17	24	25	20 3	13	12
5 7 49	18	25	26	20 49	14	13
5 12 9	19	25	27	21 35	14	14
5 16 29	20	26	28	22 20	15	14
5 20 49	21	27	28	23 6	16	15
5 25 9	22	28	29	23 51	17	16
5 29 30	23	29	0♍	24 37	18	17
5 33 51	24	0♌	1	25 23	19	18
5 38 12	25	1	2	26 9	20	19
5 42 34	26	2	3	26 55	21	20
5 46 55	27	3	4	27 41	21	21
5 51 17	28	4	4	28 27	22	22
5 55 38	29	5	5	29 13	23	23
6 0 0	0	6	6	0 0	24	24

Sidereal Time	10 ♋	11 ♌	12 ♍	Ascen ♎	2 ♎	3 ♏
H. M. S.	°	°	°	° °	°	°
6 0 0	0	6	6	0 0	24	24
6 4 22	1	7	7	0 47	25	25
6 8 43	2	8	8	1 33	26	26
6 13 5	3	9	9	2 19	27	27
6 17 26	4	10	10	3 5	27	28
6 21 48	5	11	10	3 51	28	29
6 26 9	6	12	11	4 37	29	0♐
6 30 30	7	13	12	5 23	0♏	1
6 34 51	8	14	13	6 9	1	2
6 39 11	9	15	14	6 55	2	3
6 43 31	10	16	15	7 40	2	4
6 47 51	11	16	16	8 26	3	4
6 52 11	12	17	16	9 12	4	5
6 56 31	13	18	17	9 58	5	6
7 0 50	14	19	18	10 43	6	7
7 5 8	15	20	19	11 28	7	8
7 9 26	16	21	20	12 14	8	9
7 13 44	17	22	21	12 59	8	10
7 18 1	18	23	22	13 45	9	11
7 22 18	19	24	23	14 30	10	12
7 26 34	20	25	24	15 11	11	13
7 30 50	21	26	25	16 0	12	14
7 35 5	22	27	25	16 45	13	15
7 39 20	23	28	26	17 30	13	16
7 43 34	24	29	27	18 14	14	17
7 47 47	25	0♍	28	18 59	15	18
7 52 0	26	1	29	19 43	16	19
7 56 12	27	2	0♎	20 27	17	20
8 0 24	28	3	0	21 11	18	20
8 4 35	29	4	1	21 56	18	21
8 8 45	30	5	2	22 40	19	22

Sidereal Time	10 ♌	11 ♍	12 ♎	Ascen ♏	2 ♏	3 ♐
H. M. S.	°	°	°	° °	°	°
8 8 45	0	5	2	22 40	19	22
8 12 54	1	5	3	23 24	20	23
8 17 3	2	6	3	24 7	21	24
8 21 11	3	7	4	24 50	22	25
8 25 19	4	8	5	25 34	23	26
8 29 26	5	9	6	26 18	23	27
8 33 31	6	10	7	27 1	24	28
8 37 37	7	11	8	27 44	25	28
8 41 41	8	12	8	28 26	26	0♑
8 45 45	9	13	9	29 9	27	1
8 49 48	10	14	10	29 53	28	2
8 53 52	11	15	11	0♏ 36	28	3
8 57 52	12	16	12	1 15	29	4
9 1 53	13	17	13	2 0	0♐	4
9 5 53	14	18	13	2 41	1	5
9 9 53	15	18	14	3 21	1	6
9 13 52	16	19	15	4 3	2	7
9 17 50	17	20	16	4 44	3	8
9 21 47	18	21	16	5 26	3	9
9 25 44	19	22	17	6 7	4	10
9 29 40	20	23	18	6 48	5	11
9 33 35	21	24	18	7 29	5	12
9 37 29	22	25	19	8 9	6	13
9 41 23	23	26	20	8 50	7	14
9 45 16	24	27	21	9 30	7	15
9 49 9	25	28	22	10 11	8	16
9 53 1	26	29	22	10 51	9	17
9 56 52	27	0♎	23	11 32	10	18
10 0 43	28	1	24	12 12	11	19
10 4 33	29	2	25	12 53	12	20
10 8 23	30	2	26	13 33	13	20

Sidereal Time	10 ♍	11 ♎	12 ♏	Ascen ♏	2 ♐	3 ♑
H. M. S.	°	°	°	° °	°	°
10 8 23	0	2	26	13 33	13	20
10 12 12	1	3	26	14 13	14	21
10 16 10	2	4	27	14 53	15	22
10 19 48	3	5	28	15 33	15	23
10 23 35	4	6	29	16 13	16	24
10 27 22	5	6	29	16 52	17	25
10 31 8	6	7	0♏	17 32	18	26
10 34 54	7	8	1	18 12	19	27
10 38 40	8	9	2	18 52	20	28
10 42 25	9	10	2	19 31	20	29
10 46 9	10	11	3	20 11	21	0♒
10 49 53	11	11	4	20 49	22	1
10 53 37	12	12	4	21 30	23	2
10 57 20	13	13	5	22 10	23	4
11 1 3	14	14	6	22 49	24	4
11 4 46	15	15	7	23 29	25	5
11 8 16	16	16	7	24 8	26	6
11 12 10	17	17	8	24 47	27	8
11 15 52	18	18	9	25 26	27	9
11 19 34	19	18	10	26 6	28	10
11 23 15	20	19	10	26 45	29	11
11 26 56	21	20	11	27 25	0♑	13
11 30 37	22	21	12	28 5	1	13
11 34 18	23	22	13	28 44	2	14
11 37 58	24	23	13	29 23	3	15
11 41 39	25	23	14	0♐ 3	4	16
11 45 19	26	24	15	0 43	5	17
11 49 0	27	25	15	1 23	6	18
11 52 40	28	26	16	2 3	6	19
11 56 20	29	27	17	2 43	7	20
12 0 0	0	27	17	3 23	8	21

TABLES OF HOUSES FOR LONDON, Latitude 51° 32′ N.

Sidereal Time H. M. S.	10 ≏	11 ≏	12 ♏	Ascen ♐ ° ′	2 ♑	3 ♒
12 0 0	0	27	17	3 23	8	21
12 3 40	1	28	18	4 4	9	23
12 7 20	2	29	19	4 45	10	24
12 11 0	3	♏	20	5 26	11	25
12 14 41	4	1	20	6 7	12	26
12 18 21	5	1	21	6 48	13	27
12 22 2	6	2	22	7 29	14	28
12 25 42	7	3	23	8 10	15	29
12 29 23	8	4	23	8 51	16	♓
12 33 4	9	5	24	9 33	17	2
12 36 45	10	6	25	10 15	18	3
12 40 26	11	6	25	10 57	19	4
12 44 8	12	7	26	11 40	20	5
12 47 50	13	8	27	12 22	21	6
12 51 32	14	9	28	13 4	22	7
12 55 14	15	10	28	13 47	23	9
12 58 57	16	11	29	14 30	24	10
13 2 40	17	11	♐	15 14	25	11
13 6 23	18	12	1	15 59	26	12
13 10 7	19	13	1	16 44	27	13
13 13 51	20	14	2	17 29	28	15
13 17 35	21	15	3	18 14	29	16
13 21 20	22	16	4	19 0	♒	17
13 25 6	23	16	4	19 45	1	18
13 28 52	24	17	5	20 31	2	20
13 32 38	25	18	6	21 18	4	21
13 36 25	26	19	7	22 6	5	22
13 40 12	27	20	7	22 54	6	23
13 44 0	28	21	8	23 42	7	25
13 47 48	29	21	9	24 31	8	26
13 51 37	30	22	10	25 20	10	27

Sidereal Time H. M. S.	10 ♏	11 ♏	12 ♐	Ascen ♐ ° ′	2 ♒	3 ♓
13 51 37	0	22	10	25 20	10	27
13 55 27	1	23	11	26 10	11	28
13 59 17	2	24	11	27 2	12	♈
14 3 8	3	25	12	27 53	14	1
14 6 59	4	26	13	28 45	15	2
14 10 51	5	26	14	29 36	16	4
14 14 44	6	27	15	0 ♑ 29	18	5
14 18 37	7	28	15	1 23	19	6
14 22 31	8	29	16	2 18	20	8
14 26 25	9	♐	17	3 14	22	9
14 30 20	10	1	18	4 11	23	10
14 34 16	11	2	19	5 9	25	11
14 38 13	12	2	20	6 7	26	13
14 42 10	13	3	20	7 6	28	14
14 46 8	14	4	21	8 6	29	15
14 50 7	15	5	22	9 8	♈	17
14 54 7	16	6	23	10 11	2	18
14 58 7	17	7	24	11 15	4	19
15 2 8	18	8	25	12 20	6	21
15 6 9	19	9	26	13 26	7	22
15 10 12	20	9	27	14 35	9	23
15 14 15	21	10	27	15 43	11	24
15 18 19	22	11	28	16 52	13	26
15 22 23	23	12	29	18 3	14	27
15 26 29	24	13	♑	19 15	16	28
15 30 35	25	14	1	20 32	17	29
15 34 41	26	15	2	21 49	18	♉
15 38 49	27	16	3	23 8	21	2
15 42 57	28	17	4	24 29	22	3
15 47 6	29	18	5	25 51	24	4
15 51 15	30	18	6	27 15	26	6

Sidereal Time H. M. S.	10 ♐	11 ♐	12 ♑	Ascen ♑ ° ′	2 ♓	3 ♉
15 51 15	0	18	6	27 15	26	6
15 55 25	1	19	7	28 42	28	7
15 59 36	2	20	8	0 ♒ 11	♈	9
16 3 48	3	21	9	1 42	2	10
16 8 0	4	22	10	3 16	3	11
16 12 13	5	23	11	4 53	5	12
16 16 26	6	24	12	6 32	7	14
16 20 40	7	25	13	8 13	9	15
16 24 55	8	26	14	9 57	11	16
16 29 10	9	27	16	11 44	12	17
16 33 26	10	28	17	13 34	14	18
16 37 42	11	29	18	15 26	16	20
16 41 59	12	♑	19	17 20	18	21
16 46 16	13	1	20	19 18	20	22
16 50 34	14	2	21	21 22	21	23
16 54 52	15	3	22	23 29	23	25
16 59 10	16	4	24	25 36	25	26
17 3 29	17	5	25	27 46	27	27
17 7 49	18	6	26	0 ♓ 28	0 ♉	28
17 12 9	19	7	27	2 19	♉	29
17 16 29	20	8	29	4 40	2	♊
17 20 49	21	9	♒	7 2	3	1
17 25 9	22	10	1	9 26	5	2
17 29 30	23	11	3	11 54	7	3
17 33 51	24	12	4	14 24	8	5
17 38 12	25	13	5	17 0	10	6
17 42 34	26	14	7	19 33	11	7
17 46 55	27	15	8	22 6	13	9
17 51 17	28	16	10	24 40	14	10
17 55 38	29	17	11	27 20	16	10
18 0 0	30	18	13	30 0	18	11

Sidereal Time H. M. S.	10 ♑	11 ♑	12 ♒	Ascen ♈ ° ′	2 ♉	3 ♊
18 0 0	0	18	13	0 0	17	11
18 4 22	1	20	14	2 39	19	13
18 8 43	2	21	16	5 19	20	14
18 13 5	3	22	17	7 55	22	15
18 17 26	4	23	19	10 29	23	16
18 21 48	5	24	20	13 2	25	17
18 26 9	6	25	22	15 36	26	18
18 30 30	7	26	23	18 6	28	19
18 34 51	8	27	25	20 34	29	20
18 39 11	9	29	27	22 59	♊	21
18 43 31	10	♒	28	25 22	1	22
18 47 51	11	1	♈	27 42	2	23
18 52 11	12	2	2	29 57	4	24
18 56 31	13	3	3	2 ♉ 8	5	25
19 0 50	14	4	5	4 24	6	26
19 5 8	15	6	7	6 30	8	27
19 9 26	16	7	9	8 36	9	28
19 13 44	17	8	10	10 40	10	29
19 18 1	18	9	12	12 39	11	♋
19 22 18	19	10	14	14 35	12	1
19 26 34	20	12	16	16 28	13	2
19 30 50	21	13	18	17 14	13	3
19 35 5	22	14	19	20 3	14	4
19 39 20	23	15	21	21 48	15	5
19 43 34	24	16	23	23 29	16	6
19 47 47	25	18	25	25 9	17	7
19 52 0	26	19	26	26 45	18	8
19 56 12	27	20	28	28 18	19	9
20 0 24	28	21	♈	29 49	20	10
20 4 35	29	23	2	1 ♊ 1	22	11
20 8 45	30	24	4	2 45	24	12

Sidereal Time H. M. S.	10 ♒	11 ♒	12 ♈	Ascen ♉ ° ′	2 ♊	3 ♋
20 8 45	0	24	4	2 45	24	12
20 12 54	1	25	6	4 9	25	12
20 17 3	2	27	7	5 32	26	13
20 21 11	3	28	9	6 53	27	14
20 25 19	4	29	11	8 12	28	15
20 29 26	5	♈	13	9 27	29	16
20 33 31	6	2	14	10 43	♋	17
20 37 37	7	3	16	11 58	1	18
20 41 41	8	4	18	13 9	2	19
20 45 45	9	6	19	14 18	3	20
20 49 48	10	7	21	15 25	3	21
20 53 51	11	8	23	16 32	4	22
20 57 52	12	9	24	17 39	5	23
21 1 53	13	11	26	18 44	6	23
21 5 53	14	12	28	19 48	7	24
21 9 53	15	13	29	20 51	8	25
21 13 52	16	15	♉	21 53	9	26
21 17 50	17	16	2	22 53	10	27
21 21 47	18	17	4	23 52	11	28
21 25 44	19	19	5	24 51	11	29
21 29 40	20	20	7	25 48	12	29
21 33 31	21	21	8	26 44	13	♌
21 37 29	22	23	10	27 40	14	1
21 41 23	23	24	11	28 34	15	2
21 45 16	24	25	13	29 29	15	3
21 49 9	25	26	14	0 ♊ 22	16	4
21 53 1	26	28	15	1 26	17	5
21 56 52	27	29	16	2 18	18	5
22 0 43	28	♈	18	2 57	19	6
22 4 33	29	2	19	3 48	19	7
22 8 23	30	3	20	4 38	20	8

Sidereal Time H. M. S.	10 ♓	11 ♈	12 ♉	Ascen ♊ ° ′	2 ♋	3 ♌
22 8 23	0	3	20	4 38	20	8
22 12 12	1	4	21	5 28	21	8
22 16 0	2	6	23	6 17	22	9
22 19 48	3	7	24	7 5	23	10
22 23 35	4	8	25	7 53	23	11
22 27 22	5	9	26	8 42	24	12
22 31 8	6	10	28	9 29	25	13
22 34 54	7	12	29	10 16	26	14
22 38 40	8	13	♊	11 0	26	14
22 42 25	9	14	1	11 47	27	15
22 46 9	10	15	2	12 31	28	16
22 49 53	11	17	3	13 13	29	17
22 53 37	12	18	4	13 55	29	18
22 57 20	13	19	5	14 45	♌	19
23 1 3	14	20	6	15 28	1	19
23 4 46	15	21	7	16 11	2	20
23 8 28	16	23	8	16 54	3	21
23 12 10	17	24	9	17 37	3	22
23 15 52	18	25	10	18 20	4	23
23 19 34	19	26	11	19 3	5	24
23 23 15	20	27	12	19 45	5	24
23 26 56	21	29	13	20 26	6	25
23 30 37	22	♉	14	21 8	7	26
23 34 18	23	1	15	21 50	8	27
23 37 58	24	2	16	22 32	8	28
23 41 39	25	3	17	23 12	9	28
23 45 19	26	4	18	23 53	10	29
23 49 0	27	5	19	24 32	11	♍
23 52 40	28	6	20	25 15	11	1
23 56 20	29	8	21	25 56	12	2
24 0 0	30	9	22	26 36	13	3

TABLES OF HOUSES FOR LIVERPOOL, Latitude 53° 25′ N.

Block 1

Sidereal Time (H. M. S.)	10 ♈	11 ♉	12 ♊	Ascen ♋	2 ♌	3 ♍
0 0 0	0	9	24	28 12	14	3
0 3 40	1	10	25	28 51	14	4
0 7 20	2	12	25	29 30	15	4
0 11 0	3	13	26	0♌ 9	16	5
0 14 41	4	14	27	0 48	17	6
0 18 21	5	15	28	1 27	17	7
0 22 2	6	16	29	2 6	18	8
0 25 42	7	17	♋	2 44	19	9
0 29 23	8	18	1	3 22	19	10
0 33 4	9	19	1	4 1	20	10
0 36 45	10	20	2	4 39	21	11
0 40 26	11	21	3	5 18	22	12
0 44 8	12	22	4	5 56	22	13
0 47 50	13	23	5	6 34	23	14
0 51 32	14	24	6	7 13	24	14
0 55 14	15	25	6	7 51	24	15
0 58 57	16	26	7	8 30	25	16
1 2 40	17	27	8	9 8	26	17
1 6 23	18	28	9	9 47	26	18
1 10 7	19	29	10	10 25	27	19
1 13 51	20	♊	11	11 4	28	19
1 17 35	21	1	11	11 43	28	20
1 21 20	22	2	12	12 21	29	21
1 25 6	23	3	13	13 0	♍	22
1 28 52	24	4	14	13 38	1	23
1 32 38	25	5	15	14 17	1	24
1 36 25	26	6	15	14 56	2	25
1 40 12	27	7	16	15 35	3	26
1 44 0	28	8	17	16 14	3	26
1 47 48	30	9	18	16 53	4	27

Block 2

Sidereal Time (H. M. S.)	10 ♉	11 ♊	12 ♋	Ascen ♌	2 ♍	3 ♍
1 51 37	0	10	18	17 32	5	28
1 55 27	1	11	19	18 11	6	29
1 59 17	2	12	20	18 51	6	♎
2 3 8	3	13	21	19 30	7	1
2 6 59	4	14	22	20 9	8	2
2 10 51	5	15	22	20 49	9	2
2 14 44	6	16	23	21 28	9	3
2 18 37	7	17	24	22 8	10	4
2 22 31	8	18	25	22 48	11	5
2 26 25	9	19	25	23 28	12	6
2 30 20	10	20	26	24 8	12	7
2 34 16	11	21	27	24 48	13	7
2 38 13	12	22	28	25 28	14	9
2 42 10	13	23	29	26 9	15	10
2 46 8	14	24	29	26 49	15	10
2 50 7	15	25	♌	27 29	16	11
2 54 7	16	26	1	28 9	17	12
2 58 7	17	27	2	28 51	18	13
3 2 8	18	28	2	29 32	19	14
3 6 9	19	29	3	0♍13	19	15
3 10 12	20	29	4	0 54	20	16
3 14 15	21	♋	5	1 36	21	17
3 18 19	22	1	5	2 17	22	18
3 22 23	23	2	6	2 59	23	19
3 26 29	24	3	7	3 41	23	20
3 30 35	25	4	8	4 23	24	21
3 34 41	26	5	9	5 5	25	22
3 38 49	27	6	10	5 47	26	22
3 42 57	28	7	10	6 29	27	23
3 47 6	29	8	11	7 12	27	24
3 51 15	30	9	12	7 55	28	25

Block 3

Sidereal Time (H. M. S.)	10 ♊	11 ♋	12 ♌	Ascen ♍	2 ♍	3 ♎
3 51 15	0	9	12	7 55	28	25
3 55 25	1	10	13	8 37	29	26
3 59 36	2	11	13	9 20	♎	27
4 3 48	3	12	14	10 3	1	28
4 8 0	4	12	15	10 46	2	29
4 12 13	5	13	16	11 30	2	♏
4 16 26	6	14	17	12 13	3	1
4 20 40	7	15	18	12 56	4	2
4 24 55	8	16	18	13 40	5	3
4 29 10	9	17	19	14 24	6	4
4 33 26	10	18	20	15 8	7	5
4 37 42	11	19	21	15 52	7	6
4 41 59	12	20	21	16 36	8	6
4 46 16	13	21	22	17 20	9	7
4 50 34	14	22	23	18 4	10	8
4 54 52	15	23	24	18 48	11	9
4 59 10	16	24	25	19 32	12	10
5 3 29	17	24	26	20 17	12	11
5 7 49	18	25	26	21 1	13	12
5 12 9	19	26	27	21 46	14	13
5 16 29	20	27	28	22 31	15	14
5 20 49	21	28	29	23 16	16	15
5 25 9	22	29	♍	24 1	17	16
5 29 30	23	♌	1	24 45	18	17
5 33 51	24	1	1	25 30	18	18
5 38 12	25	2	2	26 15	19	19
5 42 34	26	3	3	27 0	20	20
5 46 55	27	4	4	27 45	21	21
5 51 17	28	5	5	28 30	22	21
5 55 38	29	6	6	29 15	23	22
6 0 0	30	7	7	30 0	23	23

Block 4

Sidereal Time (H. M. S.)	10 ♋	11 ♌	12 ♍	Ascen ♎	2 ♎	3 ♏
6 0 0	0	7	7	0 23	23	23
6 4 22	1	8	7	0 45	24	24
6 8 43	2	9	8	1 30	25	25
6 13 5	3	9	9	2 15	26	26
6 17 26	4	10	10	3 0	27	27
6 21 48	5	11	11	3 45	28	28
6 26 9	6	12	12	4 30	29	29
6 30 30	7	13	12	5 15	♏	♐
6 34 51	8	14	13	6 0	1	1
6 39 11	9	15	14	6 44	1	2
6 43 31	10	16	15	7 29	2	3
6 47 51	11	17	16	8 14	3	4
6 52 11	12	18	17	8 59	4	5
6 56 31	13	19	18	9 43	4	6
7 0 50	14	20	18	10 27	5	6
7 5 8	15	21	19	11 11	6	7
7 9 26	16	22	20	11 56	7	8
7 13 44	17	23	21	12 40	8	9
7 18 1	18	24	22	13 24	8	10
7 22 18	19	24	23	14 8	9	11
7 26 34	20	25	23	14 52	10	12
7 30 50	21	26	24	15 36	11	13
7 35 5	22	27	25	16 20	12	14
7 39 20	23	28	26	17 4	12	14
7 43 34	24	29	27	17 47	13	16
7 47 47	25	♍	28	18 30	14	17
7 52 0	26	1	28	19 13	15	18
7 56 12	27	2	29	19 57	16	18
8 0 24	28	3	♎	20 40	17	19
8 4 35	29	4	1	21 23	17	20
8 8 45	30	5	2	22 5	18	21

Block 5

Sidereal Time (H. M. S.)	10 ♌	11 ♍	12 ♎	Ascen ♎	2 ♏	3 ♐
8 8 45	0	5	2	22 5	18	21
8 12 54	1	6	2	22 48	19	22
8 17 3	2	7	3	23 30	20	23
8 21 11	3	8	4	24 13	20	25
8 25 19	4	8	5	24 55	21	25
8 29 26	5	9	6	25 37	22	26
8 33 37	6	10	7	26 19	23	27
8 37 37	7	11	7	27 1	24	28
8 41 41	8	12	8	27 43	25	29
8 45 45	9	13	9	28 24	25	♑
8 49 48	10	14	10	29 6	26	1
8 53 51	11	15	11	29 47	27	2
8 57 52	12	16	11	0♏29	28	2
9 1 53	13	17	12	1 9	28	3
9 5 53	14	18	13	1 50	29	4
9 9 53	15	19	14	2 31	♐	5
9 13 52	16	19	15	3 11	1	6
9 17 50	17	20	15	3 51	1	7
9 21 47	18	21	16	4 32	2	8
9 25 44	19	22	17	5 12	3	9
9 29 40	20	23	18	5 52	4	10
9 33 35	21	24	18	6 32	5	11
9 37 29	22	25	19	7 12	5	12
9 41 23	23	26	20	7 52	6	13
9 45 16	24	27	21	8 32	7	14
9 49 9	25	27	21	9 9	8	15
9 53 1	26	28	22	9 51	9	16
9 56 52	27	29	23	10 30	9	17
10 0 43	28	♎	24	11 9	10	18
10 4 33	29	1	24	11 49	11	18
10 8 23	30	2	25	12 28	11	19

Block 6

Sidereal Time (H. M. S.)	10 ♍	11 ♎	12 ♎	Ascen ♏	2 ♐	3 ♑
10 8 23	0	2	25	8 23	11	19
10 12 12	1	3	26	9 3	12	20
10 16 0	2	4	27	9 43	13	21
10 19 48	3	4	27	10 22	13	22
10 23 35	4	5	28	11 1	14	23
10 27 22	5	6	29	11 42	15	24
10 31 8	6	7	♏	12 21	16	26
10 34 54	7	8	1	13 0	17	26
10 38 40	8	9	1	13 39	17	27
10 42 25	9	10	2	14 18	18	28
10 46 9	10	10	2	14 55	19	29
10 49 53	11	11	3	15 34	19	♒
10 53 37	12	12	4	16 12	20	1
10 57 20	13	13	4	16 50	21	2
11 1 0	14	14	5	17 28	22	3
11 4 46	15	15	6	18 6	22	5
11 8 28	16	16	7	18 44	23	6
11 12 10	17	17	7	19 22	24	7
11 15 52	18	17	8	19 59	25	8
11 19 34	19	18	9	20 36	26	9
11 23 20	20	19	9	21 14	26	11
11 26 56	21	20	10	21 51	27	12
11 30 37	22	21	11	22 29	28	13
11 34 18	23	21	12	23 7	29	14
11 37 58	24	22	12	23 45	♑	14
11 41 39	25	23	13	24 23	1	15
11 45 19	26	24	13	25 19	1	16
11 49 0	27	25	14	25 50	3	17
11 52 40	28	25	15	26 28	4	18
11 56 20	29	26	16	27 9	5	20
12 0 0	0♎	27	16	27 48	6	21

TABLES OF HOUSES FOR LIVERPOOL, Latitude 53° 25′ N

Upper section

Left panel

Sidereal Time	10 ♎	11 ♏	12 ♏	Ascen ♐	2 ♒	3 ♒
H. M. S.	°	°	°	° ′	°	°
12 0 0	0	27	16	1 48	6	21
12 3 40	1	28	17	2 27	7	22
12 7 20	2	29	18	3 6	8	23
12 11 0	3	♏	18	3 46	9	24
12 14 41	4	0	19	4 25	10	25
12 18 21	5	1	20	5 6	10	26
12 22 2	6	2	21	5 46	11	28
12 25 42	7	3	21	6 26	12	29
12 29 23	8	4	22	7 6	13	♓
12 33 4	9	4	23	7 46	14	1
12 36 45	10	5	24	8 27	15	2
12 40 26	11	6	24	9 8	16	3
12 44 8	12	7	25	9 49	17	5
12 47 50	13	8	26	10 30	18	6
12 51 32	14	9	26	11 12	19	7
12 55 14	15	9	27	11 54	20	8
12 58 57	16	10	28	12 36	21	10
13 2 40	17	11	28	13 19	22	11
13 6 23	18	12	29	14 2	23	12
13 10 7	19	13	♐	14 45	25	13
13 13 51	20	13	1	15 28	26	15
13 17 35	21	14	1	16 12	27	16
13 21 20	22	15	2	16 56	28	17
13 25 6	23	16	3	17 41	29	18
13 28 52	24	17	4	18 26	♒	19
13 32 38	25	17	4	19 11	1	21
13 36 25	26	18	5	19 57	3	22
13 40 12	27	19	6	20 44	4	23
13 44 0	28	20	7	21 31	5	24
13 47 48	29	21	7	22 18	7	26
13 51 37	30	21	8	23 6	8	27

Middle panel

Sidereal Time	10 ♏	11 ♏	12 ♐	Ascen ♐	2 ♒	3 ♓
H. M. S.	°	°	°	° ′	°	°
13 51 37	0	21	8	23 6	8	27
13 55 27	1	22	9	23 55	9	28
13 59 17	2	23	10	24 43	10	♈
14 3 8	3	24	10	25 33	12	1
14 6 59	4	25	11	26 23	13	2
14 10 51	5	26	12	27 14	15	4
14 14 44	6	26	13	28 6	16	5
14 18 37	7	27	13	28 59	18	6
14 22 31	8	28	14	29 52	19	8
14 26 25	9	29	15	0 ♈ 46	20	9
14 30 20	10	♐	16	1 41	22	10
14 34 16	11	1	17	2 36	23	11
14 38 13	12	2	18	3 33	25	13
14 42 10	13	2	18	4 30	26	14
14 46 8	14	3	19	5 29	28	16
14 50 7	15	4	20	6 29	♈	17
14 54 7	16	5	21	7 30	1	18
14 58 7	17	6	22	8 32	3	20
15 2 8	18	6	22	9 35	5	21
15 6 9	19	8	24	10 39	6	22
15 10 12	20	8	24	11 45	8	23
15 14 15	21	9	25	12 52	10	25
15 18 19	22	10	26	14 1	11	26
15 22 23	23	11	27	15 11	13	28
15 26 29	24	12	28	16 23	15	29
15 30 35	25	13	29	17 37	17	♈
15 34 41	26	14	♑	18 53	18	1
15 38 49	27	15	1	20 10	21	2
15 42 57	28	16	2	21 29	22	4
15 47 6	29	16	3	22 49	24	5
15 51 15	30	17	4	24 15	26	7

Right panel

Sidereal Time	10 ♐	11 ♐	12 ♑	Ascen ♑	2 ♓	3 ♉
H. M. S.	°	°	°	° ′	°	°
15 51 15	0	17	4	24 15	26	7
15 55 25	1	18	5	25 41	28	8
15 59 36	2	19	6	27 10	♈	9
16 3 48	3	20	7	28 41	2	10
16 8 0	4	21	8	0 ♒ 14	4	12
16 12 13	5	22	9	1 50	5	13
16 16 26	6	23	10	3 30	7	14
16 20 40	7	24	11	5 13	9	15
16 24 55	8	25	12	6 58	11	17
16 29 10	9	26	13	8 46	13	18
16 33 26	10	27	14	10 38	15	19
16 37 42	11	28	15	12 32	17	20
16 41 59	12	29	16	14 31	19	22
16 46 16	13	♑	18	16 33	20	23
16 50 34	14	1	19	18 40	22	24
16 54 52	15	2	20	20 50	24	25
16 59 10	16	3	21	23 4	26	26
17 3 29	17	4	22	25 21	28	28
17 7 49	18	5	24	27 42	29	29
17 12 9	19	6	25	0 ♉ 8	0	♊
17 16 29	20	7	26	2 37	3	1
17 20 49	21	8	28	5 10	5	3
17 25 9	22	9	29	7 46	6	4
17 29 30	23	10	♒	10 24	8	5
17 33 51	24	11	2	13 7	10	6
17 38 12	25	12	3	15 52	11	7
17 42 34	26	13	4	18 38	13	8
17 46 55	27	14	6	21 27	15	9
17 51 17	28	15	7	24 17	16	10
17 55 38	29	16	9	27 8	18	12
18 0 0	30	17	11	0 0	19	13

Lower section

Left panel

Sidereal Time	10 ♑	11 ♑	12 ♒	Ascen ♈	2 ♉	3 ♊
H. M. S.	°	°	°	° ′	°	°
18 0 0	0	17	11	0 0	19	13
18 4 22	1	18	12	2 52	21	14
18 8 43	2	20	14	5 43	23	15
18 13 5	3	21	15	8 33	24	16
18 17 26	4	22	17	11 22	25	17
18 21 48	5	23	19	14 8	27	18
18 26 9	6	24	20	16 53	28	19
18 30 30	7	25	22	19 36	29	20
18 34 51	8	26	24	22 14	1	21
18 39 11	9	27	25	24 50	2	22
18 43 31	10	29	27	27 23	4	23
18 47 51	11	♒	28	29 52	5	24
18 52 11	12	1	♈	2 ♉ 18	6	25
18 56 31	13	2	2	4 39	8	26
19 0 50	14	4	4	6 56	9	27
19 5 8	15	5	6	9 10	10	28
19 9 26	16	6	8	11 20	11	29
19 13 44	17	7	10	13 27	12	♋
19 18 1	18	8	11	15 29	14	1
19 22 18	19	9	13	17 28	15	2
19 26 34	20	11	15	19 22	16	3
19 30 50	21	12	17	21 14	17	4
19 35 5	22	13	19	23 2	18	5
19 39 20	23	15	21	24 47	19	6
19 43 34	24	16	23	26 30	20	7
19 47 47	25	17	25	28 10	21	8
19 52 0	26	18	26	29 46	22	9
19 56 12	27	20	28	1 ♊ 19	23	10
20 0 24	28	21	♈	2 50	24	11
20 4 35	29	22	2	4 19	25	12
20 8 45	30	23	4	5 45	26	13

Middle panel

Sidereal Time	10 ♒	11 ♒	12 ♈	Ascen ♊	2 ♊	3 ♋
H. M. S.	°	°	°	° ′	°	°
20 8 45	0	23	4	5 45	26	13
20 12 54	1	25	6	7 9	27	14
20 17 3	2	26	8	8 31	28	14
20 21 11	3	27	9	9 50	29	15
20 25 19	4	29	11	11 7	♋	16
20 29 26	5	♓	13	12 24	1	17
20 33 31	6	1	14	13 35	1	18
20 37 37	7	3	16	14 47	2	19
20 41 41	8	4	17	15 59	3	20
20 45 45	9	5	20	17 8	5	21
20 49 48	10	7	22	18 15	6	22
20 53 51	11	8	24	19 22	7	23
20 57 52	12	9	25	20 28	8	24
21 1 53	13	11	27	21 33	8	24
21 5 53	14	12	28	22 37	9	25
21 9 53	15	13	♉	23 40	10	26
21 13 52	16	15	1	24 43	11	27
21 17 50	17	16	3	25 44	12	28
21 21 47	18	17	4	26 44	13	29
21 25 44	19	18	6	27 44	14	♌
21 29 40	20	20	8	28 43	15	1
21 33 35	21	21	9	29 41	15	1
21 37 29	22	22	11	0 ♋ 38	16	2
21 41 23	23	23	12	1 24	17	3
21 45 16	24	25	13	2 10	18	4
21 49 9	25	26	15	2 57	19	5
21 53 1	26	27	16	3 44	19	5
21 56 52	27	29	18	4 31	20	6
22 0 43	28	♈	19	5 18	21	7
22 4 33	29	2	21	6 6	22	7
22 8 23	30	3	22	6 54	22	8

Right panel

Sidereal Time	10 ♓	11 ♈	12 ♉	Ascen ♋	2 ♋	3 ♌
H. M. S.	°	°	°	° ′	°	°
22 8 23	0	3	22	6 54	22	8
22 12 12	1	4	23	7 42	23	9
22 16 0	2	5	25	8 29	23	10
22 19 48	3	7	26	9 16	24	11
22 23 35	4	8	27	10 3	25	12
22 27 22	5	9	29	10 49	26	13
22 31 8	6	11	♊	11 34	27	14
22 34 54	7	12	1	12 19	27	14
22 38 40	8	13	2	13 4	28	15
22 42 25	9	14	3	13 48	29	16
22 46 9	10	16	4	14 32	♌	17
22 49 53	11	17	5	15 15	1	18
22 53 37	12	18	7	15 57	1	18
22 57 23	13	19	8	16 41	2	19
23 1 3	14	20	9	17 24	2	20
23 4 46	15	22	11	18 6	3	21
23 8 26	16	23	11	18 48	4	21
23 12 10	17	24	12	19 30	4	22
23 15 52	18	25	14	20 11	5	23
23 19 34	19	27	14	20 52	6	24
23 23 15	20	28	15	21 33	6	25
23 26 14	21	29	16	22 14	7	26
23 30 37	22	♉	17	22 54	8	26
23 34 18	23	1	18	23 34	9	27
23 37 58	24	2	19	24 14	9	28
23 41 39	25	4	20	24 54	10	29
23 45 19	26	5	21	25 35	11	♍
23 49 0	27	6	22	26 14	11	1
23 52 40	28	7	22	26 54	12	1
23 56 20	29	8	23	27 33	13	2
24 0 0	30	9	24	28 12	14	3

TABLES OF HOUSES FOR NEW YORK, Latitude 40° 43′ N.

Sidereal Time H. M. S.	10 ♈	11 ♉	12 ♊	Ascen ♋ °	′	2 ♌	3 ♍
0 0 0	0	6	15	18	53	8	1
0 3 40	1	7	16	19	38	9	2
0 7 20	2	8	17	20	23	10	3
0 11 0	3	9	18	21	9	11	4
0 14 41	4	11	19	21	55	12	5
0 18 21	5	12	20	22	40	12	5
0 22 2	6	13	21	23	24	13	6
0 25 42	7	14	22	24	8	14	7
0 29 23	8	15	23	24	54	15	8
0 33 4	9	16	23	25	37	15	9
0 36 45	10	17	24	26	22	16	10
0 40 26	11	18	25	27	5	17	11
0 44 8	12	19	26	27	50	18	12
0 47 50	13	20	27	28	33	19	13
0 51 32	14	21	28	29	18	19	13
0 55 14	15	22	28	0♌	3	20	14
0 58 57	16	23	29	0	46	21	15
1 2 40	17	24	♋	1	31	22	16
1 6 23	18	25	1	2	14	22	17
1 10 7	19	26	2	2	58	23	18
1 13 51	20	27	3	3	43	24	19
1 17 35	21	28	3	4	27	25	20
1 21 20	22	29	4	5	12	25	21
1 25 6	23	♊	5	5	56	26	22
1 28 52	24	1	6	6	40	27	22
1 32 38	25	2	7	7	25	28	23
1 36 25	26	2	8	8	9	29	24
1 40 12	27	3	9	8	53	♍	25
1 44 0	28	4	10	9	38	1	26
1 47 48	29	5	10	10	24	1	27
1 51 37	30	6	11	11	8	2	28

Sidereal Time H. M. S.	10 ♉	11 ♊	12 ♋	Ascen ♌ °	′	2 ♍	3 ♍
1 51 37	0	6	11	11	8	2	28
1 55 27	1	7	12	11	53	3	29
1 59 17	2	8	13	12	38	4	♎
2 3 8	3	9	14	13	22	5	1
2 6 59	4	10	15	14	8	5	2
2 10 51	5	11	15	14	53	6	3
2 14 44	6	12	16	15	39	7	4
2 18 37	7	13	17	16	24	8	4
2 22 31	8	14	18	17	10	9	5
2 26 25	9	15	19	17	56	10	6
2 30 20	10	16	20	18	41	10	7
2 34 16	11	17	20	19	27	11	8
2 38 13	12	18	21	20	14	12	9
2 42 10	13	19	22	21	0	13	10
2 46 8	14	19	23	21	47	14	11
2 50 7	15	20	24	22	33	15	12
2 54 7	16	21	25	23	20	16	13
2 58 7	17	22	25	24	7	17	14
3 2 8	18	23	26	24	54	17	15
3 6 9	19	24	27	25	42	18	16
3 10 12	20	25	28	26	29	19	17
3 14 15	21	26	29	27	17	20	18
3 18 19	22	27	♌	28	4	21	19
3 22 23	23	28	1	28	52	22	20
3 26 29	24	29	1	29	40	23	21
3 30 35	25	♋	2	0♍	29	24	22
3 34 41	26	1	3	1	17	24	23
3 38 49	27	2	4	2	6	25	24
3 42 57	28	3	5	2	55	26	25
3 47 6	29	4	6	3	43	27	26
3 51 15	30	5	7	4	32	28	27

Sidereal Time H. M. S.	10 ♊	11 ♋	12 ♌	Ascen ♍ °	′	2 ♍	3 ♎
3 51 15	0	5	7	4	32	28	27
3 55 25	1	6	8	5	22	29	28
3 59 36	2	6	8	6	10	♎	29
4 3 48	3	7	9	7	0	1	♏
4 8 0	4	8	10	7	49	2	1
4 12 13	5	9	11	8	40	3	2
4 16 26	6	10	12	9	30	4	3
4 20 40	7	11	13	10	19	4	4
4 24 55	8	12	14	11	10	5	5
4 29 10	9	13	15	12	0	6	6
4 33 26	10	14	16	12	51	7	7
4 37 42	11	15	16	13	41	8	8
4 41 59	12	16	17	14	32	9	9
4 46 16	13	17	18	15	23	10	10
4 50 34	14	18	19	16	14	11	11
4 54 52	15	19	20	17	5	12	12
4 59 10	16	20	21	17	56	13	13
5 3 29	17	21	22	18	47	14	14
5 7 49	18	22	23	19	39	15	15
5 12 9	19	23	24	19	30	16	16
5 16 29	20	24	25	21	22	17	17
5 20 49	21	25	25	22	13	18	18
5 25 9	22	26	26	23	5	18	19
5 29 30	23	27	27	23	57	19	20
5 33 51	24	28	28	24	49	20	21
5 38 12	25	29	29	25	40	21	22
5 42 34	26	♌	♍	26	32	22	22
5 46 55	27	1	1	27	25	23	23
5 51 17	28	2	2	28	16	24	24
5 55 38	29	3	3	29	8	25	25
6 0 0	30	4	4	♎	0	26	26

Sidereal Time H. M. S.	10 ♋	11 ♌	12 ♍	Ascen ♎ °	′	2 ♎	3 ♏
6 0 0	0	4	4	0	26	26	26
6 4 22	1	5	5	0	52	27	27
6 8 43	2	6	6	1	44	28	28
6 13 5	3	6	7	2	35	29	29
6 17 26	4	7	8	3	28	♏	1
6 21 48	5	8	9	4	20	1	1
6 26 9	6	9	10	5	11	2	2
6 30 30	7	10	11	6	3	3	3
6 34 51	8	11	12	6	55	3	4
6 39 11	9	12	13	7	47	4	5
6 43 31	10	13	14	8	38	5	6
6 47 51	11	14	15	9	30	6	7
6 52 11	12	15	15	10	21	7	8
6 56 31	13	16	16	11	13	8	9
7 0 50	14	17	17	12	4	9	10
7 5 8	15	18	18	12	55	10	11
7 9 26	16	19	19	13	46	11	12
7 13 44	17	20	20	14	37	12	13
7 18 1	18	21	21	15	28	13	14
7 22 18	19	22	22	16	19	14	15
7 26 34	20	23	23	17	9	14	16
7 30 50	21	24	23	18	0	15	17
7 35 5	22	25	24	18	50	16	18
7 39 20	23	26	25	19	41	17	19
7 43 34	24	27	26	20	30	18	20
7 47 47	25	28	27	21	20	19	21
7 52 0	26	29	28	22	11	20	22
7 56 12	27	♍	29	23	0	21	23
8 0 24	28	1	♎	23	50	21	24
8 4 35	29	2	1	24	38	22	24
8 8 45	30	3	2	25	28	23	25

Sidereal Time H. M. S.	10 ♌	11 ♍	12 ♎	Ascen ♎ °	′	2 ♏	3 ♐
8 8 45	0	3	2	25	28	23	25
8 12 54	1	4	3	26	17	24	26
8 17 3	2	5	4	27	5	25	27
8 21 11	3	6	5	27	54	26	28
8 25 19	4	7	6	28	43	27	29
8 29 26	5	8	7	29	31	28	♐
8 33 31	6	9	7	0♏	20	28	1
8 37 37	7	10	8	1	8	29	2
8 41 41	8	11	9	1	56	♐	3
8 45 45	9	12	9	2	43	1	4
8 49 48	10	13	11	3	31	2	5
8 53 51	11	14	12	4	18	3	6
8 57 52	12	15	12	5	6	4	7
9 1 53	13	16	13	5	53	5	8
9 5 53	14	17	14	6	40	6	9
9 9 53	15	18	15	7	27	6	10
9 13 52	16	19	16	8	13	7	11
9 17 50	17	20	17	9	0	8	11
9 21 47	18	21	18	9	46	9	12
9 25 44	19	22	19	10	33	10	13
9 29 40	20	23	20	11	19	10	14
9 33 35	21	24	20	12	4	11	14
9 37 29	22	24	21	12	50	12	16
9 41 23	23	25	22	13	36	13	17
9 45 16	24	26	23	14	21	14	18
9 49 9	25	27	24	15	7	15	19
9 53 1	26	28	24	15	52	15	20
9 56 52	27	29	25	16	38	16	21
10 0 43	28	♎	26	17	22	17	22
10 4 33	29	1	27	18	7	18	23
10 8 23	30	2	28	18	52	19	24

Sidereal Time H. M. S.	10 ♍	11 ♎	12 ♏	Ascen ♏ °	′	2 ♐	3 ♑
10 8 23	0	2	28	18	52	19	24
10 12 12	1	3	29	19	36	20	25
10 16 0	2	4	29	20	22	20	26
10 19 48	3	5	♏	21	7	21	27
10 23 35	4	6	1	21	52	22	28
10 27 22	5	7	1	22	35	23	28
10 31 8	6	7	2	23	20	24	29
10 34 54	7	8	3	24	4	25	♑
10 38 40	8	9	4	24	48	25	1
10 42 25	9	10	5	25	32	26	2
10 46 9	10	11	6	26	17	27	3
10 49 53	11	12	7	27	2	28	4
10 53 37	12	13	7	27	46	29	6
10 57 20	13	14	8	28	29	♑	6
11 1 0	14	15	9	29	14	1	7
11 4 46	15	16	10	29	57	1	8
11 8 28	16	17	11	0♐	42	2	9
11 12 10	17	17	11	1	27	3	10
11 15 52	18	18	12	2	10	4	11
11 19 34	19	19	13	2	55	5	12
11 23 15	20	20	14	3	38	6	13
11 26 56	21	21	14	4	23	7	14
11 30 37	22	22	15	5	6	7	15
11 34 18	23	23	16	5	52	8	16
11 37 58	24	24	17	6	36	9	17
11 41 39	25	24	18	7	20	10	18
11 45 19	26	25	18	8	5	11	19
11 49 0	27	26	19	8	51	12	20
11 52 40	28	27	20	9	37	13	22
11 56 20	29	28	21	10	22	14	23
12 0 0	30	29	21	11	7	15	24

Top row of tables (Sidereal Time 12h – 17h)

Sidereal Time H.M.S.	10 ♎	11 ♎	12 ♏	Ascen ♐	2 ♑	3 ≈
12 0 0	0	29	21	11 7	15	24
12 3 40	1	♏	22	11 52	16	25
12 7 20	2	1	23	12 37	17	26
12 11 0	3	1	24	13 19	17	27
12 14 41	4	2	25	14 7	18	28
12 18 21	5	3	25	14 52	19	29
12 22 2	6	4	26	15 38	20	♓
12 25 42	7	5	27	16 23	21	1
12 29 23	8	6	28	17 11	22	2
12 33 4	9	6	28	17 58	23	3
12 36 45	10	7	29	18 45	24	4
12 40 26	11	8	♐	19 32	25	5
12 44 8	12	9	1	20 20	26	7
12 47 50	13	10	2	21 8	27	8
12 51 32	14	11	2	21 57	28	9
12 55 14	15	12	3	22 43	29	10
12 58 57	16	13	4	23 33	≈	11
13 2 40	17	13	5	24 22	1	12
13 6 23	18	14	6	25 11	2	13
13 10 7	19	15	7	26 1	3	15
13 13 51	20	16	7	26 51	5	16
13 17 35	21	17	8	27 40	6	17
13 21 20	22	18	9	28 32	7	18
13 25 5	23	19	10	29 23	8	19
13 28 52	24	19	10	0♑14	9	20
13 32 38	25	20	11	1 7	10	21
13 36 25	26	21	12	2 0	11	23
13 40 12	27	22	13	2 52	12	24
13 44 0	28	23	13	3 46	13	25
13 47 48	29	24	14	4 41	15	26
13 51 37	30	25	15	5 35	16	27

Sidereal Time H.M.S.	10 ♏	11 ♏	12 ♐	Ascen ♑	2 ≈	3 ♓
13 51 37	0	25	15	5 35	16	27
13 55 27	1	25	16	6 30	17	29
13 59 17	2	26	17	7 27	18	♈
14 3 8	3	27	18	8 23	20	1
14 6 59	4	28	18	9 20	21	2
14 10 51	5	29	19	10 18	22	3
14 14 44	6	♐	20	11 16	23	5
14 18 37	7	1	21	12 15	24	6
14 22 31	8	2	22	13 15	26	7
14 26 25	9	2	23	14 16	27	8
14 30 20	10	3	24	15 17	28	9
14 34 16	11	4	24	16 19	♈	11
14 38 13	12	5	25	17 23	1	12
14 42 10	13	6	26	18 27	2	13
14 46 8	14	7	27	19 32	4	14
14 50 7	15	8	28	20 37	5	16
14 54 7	16	9	29	21 44	6	17
14 58 7	17	10	♑	22 51	8	18
15 2 8	18	10	1	23 59	9	19
15 6 9	19	11	2	25 9	11	20
15 10 12	20	12	3	26 19	12	22
15 14 15	21	13	4	27 31	14	23
15 18 19	22	14	5	28 43	15	24
15 22 23	23	15	6	29 57	16	25
15 26 29	24	16	6	1♈14	18	26
15 30 35	25	17	7	2 28	19	28
15 34 41	26	18	8	3 46	21	29
15 38 49	27	19	9	5 5	22	♉
15 42 57	28	20	10	6 25	24	1
15 47 6	29	21	11	7 46	25	3
15 51 15	30	21	13	9 8	27	4

Sidereal Time H.M.S.	10 ♐	11 ♐	12 ♑	Ascen ≈	2 ♓	3 ♉
15 51 15	0	21	13	9 8	27	4
15 55 25	1	22	14	10 31	28	5
15 59 36	2	23	15	11 56	♈	6
16 3 48	3	24	16	13 23	1	7
16 8 0	4	25	17	14 50	3	9
16 12 13	5	26	18	16 20	4	10
16 16 26	6	27	19	17 50	6	11
16 20 40	7	28	20	19 22	7	12
16 24 55	8	29	21	20 56	9	13
16 29 10	9	♑	22	22 30	11	15
16 33 26	10	1	23	24 12	12	16
16 37 42	11	2	24	25 44	14	17
16 41 59	12	3	26	27 23	15	18
16 46 16	13	4	27	29 4	17	19
16 50 34	14	5	28	0♓45	18	20
16 54 55	15	6	29	2 27	20	22
16 59 10	16	8	≈	4 11	21	23
17 3 29	17	9	2	6 ...	22	24
17 7 49	18	9	3	8 2	23	26
17 12 9	19	10	4	9 30	26	26
17 16 29	20	11	5	11 18	27	27
17 20 49	21	12	7	13 8	29	28
17 25 9	22	13	8	14 57	♉	♊
17 29 30	23	14	9	16 48	2	1
17 33 51	24	15	10	18 41	3	2
17 38 12	25	16	12	20 33	5	3
17 42 34	26	17	13	22 26	6	4
17 46 55	27	19	14	24 19	7	5
17 51 17	28	20	16	26 12	9	6
17 55 38	29	21	17	28 10	10	7
18 0 0	30	22	18	0 0	12	9

Bottom row of tables (Sidereal Time 18h – 24h)

Sidereal Time H.M.S.	10 ♑	11 ♑	12 ≈	Ascen ♈	2 ♉	3 ♊
18 0 0	0	22	18	0 0	12	9
18 4 22	1	23	20	1 53	13	10
18 8 43	2	24	21	3 48	14	11
18 13 5	3	25	23	5 41	16	12
18 17 26	4	26	24	7 35	17	13
18 21 48	5	27	25	9 27	18	14
18 26 9	6	28	27	11 19	20	15
18 30 30	7	29	28	13 12	21	16
18 34 51	8	≈	♈	15 3	22	17
18 39 11	9	2	1	16 52	23	18
18 43 31	10	3	3	18 40	24	19
18 47 51	11	4	4	20 30	26	20
18 52 11	12	5	5	22 17	27	21
18 56 31	13	6	7	24 2	28	22
19 0 50	14	7	9	25 49	♊	23
19 5 8	15	9	10	27 33	1	24
19 9 26	16	10	12	29 15	2	25
19 13 44	17	11	13	0♉56	3	26
19 18 1	18	12	15	2 37	4	27
19 22 18	19	13	16	4 16	6	28
19 26 34	20	14	18	5 53	7	29
19 30 50	21	16	19	7 30	8	♋
19 35 5	22	17	21	9 4	9	1
19 39 20	23	18	22	10 38	10	2
19 43 34	24	19	24	12 11	11	3
19 47 47	25	20	25	13 41	12	4
19 52 0	26	21	27	15 10	13	5
19 56 12	27	23	28	16 37	14	6
20 0 24	28	24	♈	18 4	15	7
20 4 35	29	25	2	19 29	16	8
20 8 45	30	26	3	20 52	17	9

Sidereal Time H.M.S.	10 ≈	11 ≈	12 ♈	Ascen ♉	2 ♊	3 ♋
20 8 45	0	26	3	20 52	17	9
20 12 54	1	27	5	22 14	18	10
20 17 3	2	29	6	23 35	19	11
20 21 11	3	♈	8	24 55	20	11
20 25 19	4	1	9	26 14	21	12
20 29 26	5	2	11	27 32	22	13
20 33 31	6	3	12	28 46	23	14
20 37 37	7	5	14	0♊0	24	15
20 41 41	8	6	15	1 17	25	16
20 45 45	9	7	16	2 29	26	17
20 49 48	10	8	18	3 41	27	18
20 53 51	11	10	19	4 51	28	19
20 57 52	12	11	21	6 1	29	21
21 1 53	13	12	22	7 10	♋	22
21 5 53	14	13	24	8 16	1	23
21 9 53	15	14	25	9 23	2	24
21 13 52	16	16	27	10 28	3	25
21 17 50	17	17	28	11 32	4	26
21 21 47	18	18	♉	12 35	5	27
21 25 44	19	19	1	13 37	6	28
21 29 40	20	21	2	14 39	7	29
21 33 38	21	22	4	15 39	8	♌
21 37 29	22	23	5	16 39	9	1
21 41 23	23	24	6	17 38	10	2
21 45 13	24	26	7	18 37	11	3
21 49 9	25	27	9	19 35	12	4
21 53 1	26	28	10	20 32	13	5
21 56 52	27	29	12	21 29	14	6
22 0 43	28	♉	13	22 24	15	7
22 4 33	29	1	14	23 19	16	8
22 8 23	30	3	15	24 13	17	9

Sidereal Time H.M.S.	10 ♓	11 ♈	12 ♉	Ascen ♊	2 ♋	3 ♌
22 8 23	0	3	15	24 13	17	9
22 12 12	1	4	16	25 9	18	10
22 16 0	2	5	17	26 4	19	11
22 19 48	3	6	18	27 0	20	12
22 23 35	4	7	19	27 54	21	13
22 27 22	5	8	20	28 48	22	14
22 31 8	6	10	21	29 46	23	15
22 34 54	7	11	22	0♋37	24	16
22 38 40	8	12	23	1 28	25	17
22 42 25	9	13	24	2 19	26	18
22 46 9	10	14	26	3 10	27	19
22 49 53	11	15	27	4 0	28	20
22 53 37	12	16	28	4 50	29	21
22 57 20	13	18	29	5 40	♌	22
23 1 3	14	19	♊	6 30	1	23
23 4 46	15	20	1	7 18	2	24
23 8 28	16	21	2	8 5	3	25
23 12 10	17	22	3	8 52	4	26
23 15 52	18	23	4	9 38	5	27
23 19 34	19	24	5	10 24	6	28
23 23 15	20	26	6	11 9	7	29
23 26 56	21	27	7	11 54	8	♍
23 30 37	22	28	8	12 38	9	1
23 34 18	23	29	10	13 22	10	2
23 37 58	24	♈	11	14 5	11	3
23 41 39	25	1	11	14 48	12	4
23 45 19	26	2	12	15 31	13	5
23 49 0	27	3	12	16 14	14	6
23 52 40	28	4	13	16 56	15	7
23 56 20	29	5	14	17 38	16	8
24 0 0	30	6	15	18 20	17	9

PROPORTIONAL LOGARITHMS FOR FINDING THE PLANETS' PLACES

DEGREES OR HOURS

Min	0	1	2	3	4	5	6	7	8	9	10	11	12	13	14	15	Min
0	3.1584	1.3802	1.0792	9031	7781	6812	6021	5351	4771	4260	3802	3388	3010	2663	2341	2041	0
1	3.1584	1.3730	1.0756	9007	7763	6798	6009	5341	4762	4252	3795	3382	3004	2657	2336	2036	1
2	2.8573	1.3660	1.0720	8983	7745	6784	5997	5330	4753	4244	3788	3375	2998	2652	2330	2032	2
3	2.6812	1.3590	1.0685	8959	7728	6769	5985	5320	4744	4236	3780	3368	2992	2646	2325	2027	3
4	2.5563	1.3522	1.0649	8935	7710	6755	5973	5310	4735	4228	3773	3362	2986	2640	2320	2022	4
5	2.4594	1.3454	1.0614	8912	7692	6741	5961	5300	4726	4220	3766	3355	2980	2635	2315	2017	5
6	2.3802	1.3388	1.0580	8888	7674	6726	5949	5289	4717	4212	3759	3349	2974	2629	2310	2012	6
7	2.3133	1.3323	1.0546	8865	7657	6712	5937	5279	4708	4204	3752	3342	2968	2624	2305	2008	7
8	2.2553	1.3258	1.0511	8842	7639	6698	5925	5269	4699	4196	3745	3336	2962	2618	2300	2003	8
9	2.2041	1.3195	1.0478	8819	7622	6684	5913	5259	4690	4188	3737	3329	2956	2613	2295	1998	9
10	2.1584	1.3133	1.0444	8796	7604	6670	5902	5249	4682	4180	3730	3323	2950	2607	2289	1993	10
11	2.1170	1.3071	1.0411	8773	7587	6656	5890	5239	4673	4172	3723	3316	2944	2602	2284	1988	11
12	2.0792	1.3010	1.0378	8751	7570	6642	5878	5229	4664	4164	3716	3310	2938	2596	2279	1984	12
13	2.0444	1.2950	1.0345	8728	7552	6628	5866	5219	4655	4156	3709	3303	2933	2591	2274	1979	13
14	2.0122	1.2891	1.0313	8706	7535	6614	5855	5209	4646	4148	3702	3297	2927	2585	2269	1974	14
15	1.9823	1.2833	1.0280	8683	7518	6600	5843	5199	4638	4141	3695	3291	2921	2580	2264	1969	15
16	1.9542	1.2775	1.0248	8661	7501	6587	5832	5189	4629	4133	3688	3284	2915	2574	2259	1965	16
17	1.9279	1.2719	1.0216	8639	7484	6573	5820	5179	4620	4125	3681	3278	2909	2569	2254	1960	17
18	1.9031	1.2663	1.0185	8617	7467	6559	5809	5169	4611	4117	3674	3271	2903	2564	2249	1955	18
19	1.8796	1.2607	1.0153	8595	7451	6546	5797	5159	4603	4109	3667	3265	2897	2558	2244	1950	19
20	1.8573	1.2553	1.0122	8573	7434	6532	5786	5149	4594	4102	3660	3258	2891	2553	2239	1946	20
21	1.8361	1.2499	1.0091	8552	7417	6519	5774	5139	4585	4094	3653	3252	2885	2547	2234	1941	21
22	1.8159	1.2445	1.0061	8530	7401	6505	5763	5129	4577	4086	3646	3246	2880	2542	2229	1936	22
23	1.7966	1.2393	1.0030	8509	7384	6492	5752	5120	4568	4079	3639	3239	2874	2536	2223	1932	23
24	1.7781	1.2341	1.0000	8487	7368	6478	5740	5110	4559	4071	3632	3233	2868	2531	2218	1927	24
25	1.7604	1.2289	0.9970	8466	7351	6465	5729	5100	4551	4063	3625	3227	2862	2526	2213	1922	25
26	1.7434	1.2239	0.9940	8445	7335	6451	5718	5090	4542	4055	3618	3220	2856	2520	2208	1917	26
27	1.7270	1.2188	0.9910	8424	7318	6438	5706	5081	4534	4048	3611	3214	2850	2515	2203	1913	27
28	1.7112	1.2139	0.9881	8403	7302	6425	5695	5071	4525	4040	3604	3208	2845	2509	2198	1908	28
29	1.6960	1.2090	0.9852	8382	7286	6412	5684	5061	4516	4032	3597	3201	2839	2504	2193	1903	29
30	1.6812	1.2041	0.9823	8361	7270	6398	5673	5051	4508	4025	3590	3195	2833	2499	2188	1899	30
31	1.6670	1.1993	0.9794	8341	7254	6385	5662	5042	4499	4017	3583	3189	2827	2493	2183	1894	31
32	1.6532	1.1946	0.9765	8320	7238	6372	5651	5032	4491	4010	3576	3183	2821	2488	2178	1889	32
33	1.6398	1.1899	0.9737	8300	7222	6359	5640	5023	4482	4002	3570	3176	2816	2483	2173	1885	33
34	1.6269	1.1852	0.9708	8279	7206	6346	5629	5013	4474	3994	3563	3170	2810	2477	2168	1880	34
35	1.6143	1.1806	0.9680	8259	7190	6333	5618	5003	4466	3987	3556	3164	2804	2472	2164	1875	35
36	1.6021	1.1761	0.9652	8239	7174	6320	5607	4994	4457	3979	3549	3157	2798	2467	2159	1871	36
37	1.5902	1.1716	0.9625	8219	7159	6307	5596	4984	4449	3972	3542	3151	2793	2461	2154	1866	37
38	1.5786	1.1671	0.9597	8199	7143	6294	5585	4975	4440	3964	3535	3145	2787	2456	2149	1862	38
39	1.5673	1.1627	0.9570	8179	7128	6282	5574	4965	4432	3957	3529	3139	2781	2451	2144	1857	39
40	1.5563	1.1584	0.9542	8159	7112	6269	5563	4956	4424	3949	3522	3133	2775	2445	2139	1852	40
41	1.5456	1.1540	0.9515	8140	7097	6256	5552	4947	4415	3942	3515	3126	2770	2440	2134	1848	41
42	1.5351	1.1498	0.9488	8120	7081	6243	5541	4937	4407	3934	3508	3120	2764	2435	2129	1843	42
43	1.5249	1.1455	0.9462	8101	7066	6231	5531	4928	4399	3927	3501	3114	2758	2430	2124	1838	43
44	1.5149	1.1413	0.9435	8081	7050	6218	5520	4918	4390	3919	3495	3108	2753	2424	2119	1834	44
45	1.5051	1.1372	0.9409	8062	7035	6205	5509	4909	4382	3912	3488	3102	2747	2419	2114	1829	45
46	1.4956	1.1331	0.9383	8043	7020	6193	5498	4900	4374	3905	3481	3096	2741	2414	2109	1825	46
47	1.4863	1.1290	0.9356	8023	7005	6180	5488	4890	4365	3897	3475	3089	2736	2409	2104	1820	47
48	1.4771	1.1249	0.9330	8004	6990	6168	5477	4881	4357	3890	3468	3083	2730	2403	2099	1816	48
49	1.4682	1.1209	0.9305	7985	6875	6155	5466	4872	4349	3882	3461	3077	2724	2398	2095	1811	49
50	1.4594	1.1170	0.9279	7966	6960	6143	5456	4863	4341	3875	3454	3071	2719	2393	2090	1806	50
51	1.4508	1.1130	0.9254	7947	6945	6131	5445	4853	4333	3868	3448	3065	2713	2388	2085	1802	51
52	1.4424	1.1091	0.9228	7929	6930	6118	5435	4844	4324	3860	3441	3059	2707	2382	2080	1797	52
53	1.4341	1.1053	0.9203	7910	6915	6106	5424	4835	4316	3853	3434	3053	2702	2377	2075	1793	53
54	1.4260	1.1015	0.9178	7891	6900	6094	5414	4826	4308	3846	3428	3047	2696	2372	2070	1788	54
55	1.4180	1.0977	0.9153	7873	6885	6081	5403	4817	4300	3838	3421	3041	2691	2367	2065	1784	55
56	1.4102	1.0939	0.9128	7854	6871	6069	5393	4808	4292	3831	3415	3034	2685	2362	2061	1779	56
57	1.4025	1.0902	0.9104	7836	6856	6057	5382	4798	4284	3824	3408	3028	2679	2356	2056	1774	57
58	1.3949	1.0865	0.9079	7818	6841	6045	5372	4789	4276	3817	3401	3022	2674	2351	2051	1770	58
59	1.3875	1.0828	0.9055	7800	6827	6033	5361	4780	4268	3809	3395	3016	2668	2346	2046	1765	59

| 0 | 1 | 2 | 3 | 4 | 5 | 6 | 7 | 8 | 9 | 10 | 11 | 12 | 13 | 14 | 15 |

RULE:—Add proportional log. of planet's daily motion to log. of time from noon, and the sum will be the log. of the motion required. Add this to planet's place at noon, if time be p.m., but subtract if a.m. and the sum will be planet's true place. If Retrograde, subtract for p.m., but add for a.m.

What is the Long. of ☽ June 17, 1994 at 2.15 p.m.?
☽'s daily motion—14° 12'
Prop. Log. of 14° 12' .... .2279
Prop. Log. of 2h. 15m. 1.0280

☽'s motion in 2h. 15m. = 1° 20' or Log.   1.2559

☽'s Long. = 4° ♎ 48' + 1° 20' = 6° ♎ 08'
The Daily Motions of the Sun, Moon, Mercury, Venus and Mars will be found on pages 26 to 28.